Math Sprints

Workbook 4

Tricia Salerno of SMARTTraining LLC

® SingaporeMath.com Inc

SingaporeMath.com Inc

Published by
SingaporeMath.com Inc
404 Beavercreek Road #225
Oregon City, OR 97045
U.S.A.
E-mail: customerservice@singaporemath.com
www.singaporemath.com

Written by
Tricia Salerno
SMARTTraining LLC
www.SingaporeMathTraining.com

Cover design by
Jopel Multimedia

Math Sprints Workbook 4
ISBN: 978-1-932906-39-4

First published 2010 in the United States of America

Printed in Singapore

Introduction

"They don't know their facts!" This is the common lament we hear from teachers and parents around the United States. This book is here to help. Contained herein are math activities called "Sprints."

A sprint is a timed math test for FUN! That's right…There is no external pressure to achieve a certain score on sprints. The clear statement to your child that these are not for a grade should alleviate any math anxiety which sometimes arises during timed tests. It is important to let your child know that this is simply a competition against himself to improve mental math skills and it is for fun.

Act as if your child is actually involved in a race. Make it exciting. "On your mark, get set, GO!" Your child races to beat her own score and completes as many problems as possible in 60 seconds.

Importance of Math Facts

The importance of automatic recall of basic math facts has been argued in the past. In this day of technology, some say, why is it important to know the product of 6 and 8 when you can press a few buttons and have the answer quickly? In fact, you may have grown up with calculators in your hands and may have no idea how to help your child with mastering math facts because you don't know the facts yourself.

One of the problems with lack of automaticity with math facts is that if too much mental energy has to be spent recalling a basic fact, there's no mental energy left to solve the problem. Gersten and Chard stated:

> "Researchers explored the devastating effects of the lack of automaticity in several ways. Essentially they argued that the human mind has a limited capacity to process information, and if too much energy goes into figuring out what 9 plus 8 equals, little is left over to understand the concepts underlying multi-digit subtraction, long division, or complex multiplication." Gersten, R. and Chard, D. Number sense: Rethinking arithmetic instruction for students with mathematical disabilities. *Journal of Special Education* (1999), 3, 18–29 (1999).

Importance of Mental Math

Mental math is important for many reasons. Cathy Seeley, former president of the NCTM, stated:

> "Mental math is often associated with the ability to do computations quickly, but in its broadest sense, mental math also involves conceptual understanding and problem solving....Problem solving continues to be a high priority in school mathematics. Some argue that it is the most important mathematical goal for our students. Mental math provides both tools for solving problems and filters for evaluating answers. When a student has strong mental math skills, he or she can quickly test different approaches to a problem and determine whether the resulting path will lead toward a viable solution." (*NCTM News Bulletin*, December 2005).

Adrenaline

Research has proven that adrenaline aids memory. James McGaugh, a Professor of neurobiology at the University of California at Irvine, proved that adrenaline makes our brains remember better. When a sprint is given with a sense of urgency, as in a race, if your student experiences a rush of adrenaline, this can aid memory of the mental math being tested. It also makes the exercise significantly more fun!

About this Book

The Singapore Math curriculum stresses the use of mental math. These books are particularly useful to parents using Singapore Math material. In fact, sprints are useful to all parents interested in developing mental math fluency in their children.

These books were originally written for use in a classroom situation. They are reproduced here as a workbook for use in the home or in a setting with only a few students. The section below is an adaptation of how to give a sprint in a classroom situation. You can make further adaptations to meet your own child's needs, but be sure the keep it FUN! You will see that your child is racing to beat his own score each time he take one of these tests.

Each sprint is differentiated. The A sheet of each half of the sprint is easier than the B sheet. If you look closely at the A and B sheets of each sprint, the answers to the problems are the same. Many of the problems on the B sheets, however, require more mental calculation. If you have a child of average mental math abilities, you could give the A sheets first and the B sheets next, or later in the year, or not at all for that student. If you have a child that is strong in mental math abilities, you could give only the B sheet.

You may want to buy a sprint book at a level below the grade you teach so that your child gets used to taking sprints and feels very successful with them. Particularly if your child's mental math fluency is not where it should be, you can help her build it gradually by starting at a lower level.

If you are teaching more than one child, you may want to buy sprint books for each of their levels and administer the sprints to all of your children at the same time. You will have to read the answers separately for each child, though.

It is important to let your child know that this is simply a competition against himself to improve mental math skills and it is for fun. It is NOT for a grade.

How to Give a Sprint

1. Determine which sprint you want to give by looking at the topic of each. Each sprint has an A first half, an A second half, a B first half, and a B second half. The B sheets are for children stronger in math.

2. Give your child the workbook opened up to the page, face-down, of a "First Half" sheet for her to attempt to complete in 1 minute. Instruct your child not to turn the page face-up until told to "GO!" Get your child excited and enthuse: "On your mark, get set, GO!" and start your timer.

3. When the timer rings indicating one minute has elapsed, instruct your child to:

    a) stop working
    b) **draw a line under** the last problem completed
    c) put her pencil down.

4. Read the correct answers while your child pumps her hand in the air and respond "**yes**" to each problem that was answered correctly. Tell your child to mark the number of correct problems at the top of the page. If you are

administering the test to several children at different levels, you can have the other children complete the rest of the worksheet as you read the answers for one child.

5. Ask your child to complete the rest of the worksheet.
6. Let your child stand-up, stretch, run around, do jumping-jacks, etc.
7. Have your child sit back down and be ready to turn the page to do the reverse side, the second half.
8. Tell your child that the goal in this second half of the sprint is to beat his first score by at least one. **The child is competing only with himself.**
9. Repeat the preceding procedure through step 4, except that after making the correct number of problems at the top of the page, have your child compare the score on the first half to the score she got on the second half.

A good sprint:

1. Consists of two halves which test the same ONE skill. These are NOT random facts.
2. Builds in difficulty.
3. Is challenging enough that no one will be able to finish the first half in a minute.

NOTE: Look at each sprint and determine if your particular child can finish each half of a sprint in less than a minute. Some of the sprints have fewer problems than others. There is nothing wrong with doing a 30-second or 45-second sprint. Feel free to adjust the timing for your child, but be sure to keep the sense of urgency.

Acknowledgments

This series of books is due to the assistance of many people. Sprints are the brainchild of Dr. Yoram Sagher. Special thanks go to Ben Adler, Sam Adler, Laina Salerno and T. J. Salerno for their hours spent taking and re-taking the sprints contained herein. Linda West made it all come together. Thank you, thank you, thank you.

Math Sprints 4

401 A — Fill in the blank with <, >, or =. — First Half

1.	360 ______ 370	16.	3,000 + 300 ______ 300 + 3,000
2.	456 ______ 465	17.	8,000 + 4,000 _____ 8,000 + 4,010
3.	219 ______ 291	18.	8,999 + 100 ______ 8,899 + 200
4.	1,510 ______ 1,510	19.	13,000 + 525 ______ 13,515
5.	3,998 ______ 3,988	20.	42,782 _____ 40,000 + 2000 + 728
6.	14,321 ______ 14,321	21.	53,000 – 6,000 ______ 49,000
7.	32,963 ______ 33,961	22.	27,000 ______ 9,000 x 3
8.	64,219 ______ 64,199	23.	6,000 x 4 ______ 25,000
9.	100,000 ______ 99,999	24.	10,000 ÷ 2 ______ 5,500
10.	265,728 ______ 256,728	25.	16,000 ÷ 8 ______ 20,000
11.	934,400 ______ 944,999	26.	56,000 ÷ 7 ______ 6,000
12.	215,708 ______ 215,780	27.	10,000 x 10 ______ 100,000
13.	531,076 ______ 531,100	28.	102,000 ______ 50,000 x 2
14.	987,652 ______ 986,752	29.	240,000 ÷ 3 ______ 8,000
15.	842,350 ______ 852,053	30.	1,000,010 ______ 1,000,100

401 A | Fill in the blank with <, >, or =. | Second Half

1.	260 ______ 270	16.	2,000 + 200 ______ 200 + 2,000
2.	356 ______ 365	17.	5,000 + 7,000 _____ 7,000 + 5,010
3.	319 ______ 391	18.	7,999 + 100 ______ 7,899 + 200
4.	1,420 ______ 1,420	19.	12,000 + 325 ______ 12,315
5.	1,998 ______ 1,988	20.	22,782 _____ 20,000 + 2000 + 728
6.	10,324 ______ 10,324	21.	43,000 – 6,000 ______ 39,000
7.	13,965 ______ 14,963	22.	27,000 ______ 9,000 x 3
8.	18,219 ______ 18,199	23.	6,000 x 4 ______ 25,000
9.	100,000 ______ 99,999	24.	10,000 ÷ 2 ______ 5,500
10.	247,728 ______ 237,728	25.	16,000 ÷ 8 ______ 20,000
11.	934,400 ______ 944,999	26.	56,000 ÷ 7 ______ 6,000
12.	215,708 ______ 215,780	27.	10,000 x 10 ______ 100,000
13.	531,076 ______ 531,100	28.	102,000 ______ 50,000 x 2
14.	987,652 ______ 986,752	29.	240,000 ÷ 3 ______ 8,000
15.	842,350 ______ 852,053	30.	1,000,010 ______ 1,000,100

401 B — Fill in the blank with <, >, or =. — First Half

1.	3600 ______ 3700	16.	3,500 + 810 ______ 1,060 + 3,250
2.	4506 ______ 4605	17.	8,000 + 4,000 ______ 8,000 + 4,010
3.	2019 ______ 2091	18.	8,999 + 100 ______ 8,899 + 200
4.	1,510 ______ 1,000 + 510	19.	13,000 + 525 ______ 13,515
5.	3,900 + 98 ______ 3,988	20.	42,782 ______ 38,500 + 3500 + 728
6.	14,321 ______ 14,000 + 300 + 20 + 1	21.	53,000 – 6,000 ______ 49,000
7.	32,963 ______ 33,000 + 900 + 60 + 1	22.	27,000 ______ 3,000 x 3 x 3
8.	64,200 + 10 + 9 ______ 64,199	23.	2 x 6,000 x 2 ______ 25,000
9.	100,000 ______ 99,999	24.	110,000 ÷ 2 ______ 55,500
10.	265,728 ______ 255,000 + 1,728	25.	16,000 ÷ 4 ÷ 2 ______ 20,000
11.	934,400 ______ 944,999	26.	56,000 ÷ 4 ______ 2 x 2,000 x 2
12.	215,708 ______ 210,000 + 5,780	27.	10,000 x 10 ______ 100,000
13.	531,000 + 76 ______ 531,100	28.	102,000 ______ 49,000 x 2 + 2,000
14.	987,652 ______ 980,002 + 6,750	29.	240,000 ÷ 3 ______ 8,000
15.	842,350 ______ 852,053	30.	1,000,010 ______ 1,000,100

401 B Fill in the blank with <, >, or =. Second Half

1.	1600 ______ 1700	16.	3,500 + 810 _____ 1,060 + 3,250
2.	2506 ______ 2605	17.	8,000 + 4,000 _____ 8,000 + 4,010
3.	3018 ______ 3081	18.	8,999 + 100 ______ 8,899 + 200
4.	1,420 ______ 1,000 + 420	19.	13,000 + 525 ______ 13,515
5.	1,900 + 98 ______ 1,988	20.	42,782 _____ 38,500 + 3500 + 728
6.	13,361 ______ 13,000 + 300 + 60 + 1	21.	53,000 – 6,000 ______ 49,000
7.	14,963 ______ 15,000 + 900 + 60 + 3	22.	27,000 ______ 3,000 x 3 x 3
8.	64,200 + 10 + 9 ______ 64,199	23.	2 x 6,000 x 2 ______ 25,000
9.	100,000 ______ 99,999	24.	110,000 ÷ 2 ______ 55,500
10.	265,728 ______ 255,000 + 1,728	25.	16,000 ÷ 4 ÷ 2 ______ 20,000
11.	934,400 ______ 944,999	26.	56,000 ÷ 4 ______ 2 x 2,000 x 2
12.	215,708 ______ 210,000 + 5,780	27.	10,000 x 10 ______ 100,000
13.	531,000 + 76 ______ 531,100	28.	102,000 _____ 49,000 x 2 + 2,000
14.	987,652 ______ 980,002 + 6,750	29.	240,000 ÷ 3 ______ 8,000
15.	842,350 ______ 852,053	30.	1,000,010 ______ 1,000,100

402 A — Round to the nearest ten. — First Half

1.	28	19.	827
2.	34	20.	936
3.	49	21.	935
4.	65	22.	999
5.	126	23.	1,012
6.	281	24.	1,285
7.	343	25.	1,299
8.	99	26.	1,319
9.	199	27.	1,410
10.	201	28.	1,501
11.	305	29.	1,555
12.	378	30.	1,678
13.	599	31.	1,875
14.	695	32.	2,002
15.	3,652	33.	2,015
16.	800	34.	2,089
17.	792	35.	2,501
18.	815	36.	9,995

402 A — Round to the nearest ten. — Second Half

1.	27	19.	828
2.	32	20.	937
3.	48	21.	935
4.	65	22.	999
5.	127	23.	1,014
6.	283	24.	1,285
7.	342	25.	1,298
8.	99	26.	1,319
9.	199	27.	1,410
10.	203	28.	1,501
11.	305	29.	1,555
12.	379	30.	1,678
13.	598	31.	1,875
14.	695	32.	2,002
15.	3,651	33.	2,015
16.	800	34.	2,089
17.	794	35.	2,501
18.	815	36.	9,995

402 B | Round the sum to the nearest ten. | First Half

1.	27 + 1	19.	817 + 10
2.	33 + 1	20.	926 + 10
3.	48 + 1	21.	926 + 9
4.	63 + 2	22.	990 + 9
5.	124 + 2	23.	1,003 + 9
6.	279 + 2	24.	1,276 + 9
7.	341 + 2	25.	1,290 + 9
8.	96 + 3	26.	1,310 + 9
9.	196 + 3	27.	1,401 + 9
10.	198 + 3	28.	1,492 + 9
11.	302 + 3	29.	1,546 + 9
12.	374 + 4	30.	1,669 + 9
13.	595 + 4	31.	1,866 + 9
14.	691 + 4	32.	1,993 + 9
15.	3642 + 10	33.	2,006 + 9
16.	790 + 10	34.	2,078 + 11
17.	782 + 10	35.	2,490 + 11
18.	805 + 10	36.	9,984 + 11

402 B Round the sum to the nearest ten. Second Half

1.	26 + 1	19.	816 + 10
2.	32 + 1	20.	927 + 10
3.	47 + 1	21.	927 + 9
4.	63 + 2	22.	990 + 9
5.	124 + 3	23.	1,003 + 9
6.	279 + 3	24.	1,276 + 9
7.	341 + 3	25.	1,290 + 9
8.	95 + 3	26.	1,310 + 9
9.	195 + 3	27.	1,401 + 9
10.	198 + 3	28.	1,492 + 9
11.	301 + 4	29.	1,546 + 9
12.	373 + 4	30.	1,669 + 9
13.	594 + 4	31.	1,866 + 9
14.	691 + 4	32.	1,993 + 9
15.	3,643 + 10	33.	2,006 + 9
16.	790 + 10	34.	2,078 + 11
17.	783 + 10	35.	2,490 + 11
18.	805 + 10	36.	9,984 + 11

403 A   Round to the nearest hundred.   First Half

1.	128	19.	5,827
2.	134	20.	5,936
3.	149	21.	6,035
4.	165	22.	6,999
5.	286	23.	10,012
6.	292	24.	10,285
7.	363	25.	10,299
8.	599	26.	10,519
9.	889	27.	10,410
10.	1,201	28.	10,501
11.	1,305	29.	12,555
12.	1,378	30.	12,678
13.	1,599	31.	12,875
14.	2,695	32.	20,002
15.	3,652	33.	20,015
16.	4,800	34.	21,089
17.	4,590	35.	21,551
18.	4,850	36.	29,995

403 A Round to the nearest hundred. Second Half

1.	138	19.	5,838
2.	144	20.	5,926
3.	148	21.	6,049
4.	166	22.	6,999
5.	285	23.	10,045
6.	293	24.	10,255
7.	362	25.	10,299
8.	569	26.	10,519
9.	888	27.	10,410
10.	1,210	28.	10,501
11.	1,308	29.	12,555
12.	1,387	30.	12,678
13.	1,598	31.	12,875
14.	2,695	32.	20,002
15.	3,652	33.	20,015
16.	4,800	34.	21,089
17.	4,590	35.	21,551
18.	4,850	36.	29,995

403 B Round the sum to the nearest hundred. First Half

1.	127 + 1	19.	5,817 + 10
2.	133 + 1	20.	5,926 + 10
3.	148 + 1	21.	6,025 + 10
4.	164 + 1	22.	6,989 + 10
5.	284 + 2	23.	10,002 + 10
6.	290 + 2	24.	10,276 + 9
7.	360 + 3	25.	10,290 + 9
8.	596 + 3	26.	10,510 + 9
9.	886 + 3	27.	10,401 + 9
10.	1,200 + 1	28.	10,490 + 11
11.	1,300 + 5	29.	12,544 + 11
12.	1,375 + 3	30.	12,667 + 11
13.	1,596 + 3	31.	12,864 + 11
14.	2,691 + 4	32.	19, 991 + 11
15.	3,648 + 4	33.	20,004 + 11
16.	4,796 + 4	34.	21,078 + 11
17.	4,586 + 4	35.	21,540 + 11
18.	4,846 + 4	36.	29,984 + 11

403 B | Round the sum to the nearest hundred. | Second Half

1.	126 + 1	19.	5,836 + 10
2.	132 + 1	20.	5,934 + 10
3.	137 + 1	21.	6,034 + 10
4.	174 + 1	22.	6,989 + 10
5.	285 + 2	23.	10,012 + 10
6.	293 + 2	24.	10,266 + 9
7.	360 + 3	25.	10,290 + 9
8.	586 + 3	26.	10,510 + 9
9.	885 + 3	27.	10,401 + 9
10.	1,200 + 1	28.	10,490 + 11
11.	1,310 + 3	29.	12,544 + 11
12.	1,365 + 3	30.	12,667 + 11
13.	1,595 + 3	31.	12,864 + 11
14.	2,681 + 4	32.	19, 991 + 11
15.	3,648 + 4	33.	20,004 + 11
16.	4,796 + 4	34.	21,078 + 11
17.	4,586 + 4	35.	21,540 + 11
18.	4,846 + 4	36.	29,984 + 11

404 A Round to the nearest thousand. First Half

1.	128	19.	10,827
2.	334	20.	10,936
3.	449	21.	10,035
4.	565	22.	11,999
5.	1,586	23.	11,002
6.	1,792	24.	12,500
7.	2,363	25.	13,299
8.	2,599	26.	13,509
9.	2,889	27.	13,410
10.	3,201	28.	13,501
11.	4,305	29.	13,555
12.	4,478	30.	14,678
13.	4,599	31.	14,800
14.	5,795	32.	20,002
15.	6,652	33.	20,055
16.	7,800	34.	21,550
17.	8,590	35.	21,599
18.	8,850	36.	39,955

404 A Round to the nearest thousand. Second Half

1.	199	19.	10,701
2.	348	20.	10,932
3.	498	21.	10,098
4.	555	22.	11,999
5.	1,510	23.	11,028
6.	1,732	24.	12,500
7.	2,421	25.	13,499
8.	2,511	26.	13,521
9.	2,878	27.	13,389
10.	3,480	28.	13,501
11.	4,209	29.	13,555
12.	4,478	30.	14,678
13.	4,599	31.	14,800
14.	5,795	32.	20,002
15.	6,652	33.	20,099
16.	7,800	34.	21,530
17.	8,590	35.	21,599
18.	8,850	36.	39,906

404 B   Round the sum to the nearest thousand.   First Half

1.	100 + 28	19.	10,000 + 827
2.	300 + 34	20.	10,000 + 936
3.	400 + 49	21.	10,000 + 35
4.	555 + 10	22.	11,000 + 999
5.	1,576 + 10	23.	10,002 + 1,000
6.	1,782 + 10	24.	11,600 + 900
7.	2,353 + 10	25.	12,199 + 1,100
8.	2,499 + 100	26.	12,409 + 1,100
9.	2,789 + 100	27.	12,510 + 900
10.	3,101 + 100	28.	12,601 + 900
11.	4,205 + 100	29.	12,655 + 900
12.	4,378 + 100	30.	13,768 + 900
13.	3,599 + 1,000	31.	13,900 + 900
14.	4,795 + 1,000	32.	19,102 + 1,000
15.	5,652 + 1,000	33.	19,155 + 900
16.	6,800 + 1,000	34.	20,650 + 900
17.	7,490 + 1,100	35.	20,699 + 900
18.	7,750 + 1,100	36.	39,055 + 900

404 B Round the sum to the nearest thousand. Second Half

1.	100 + 82	19.	10,000 + 753
2.	300 + 53	20.	10,000 + 841
3.	400 + 99	21.	10,000 + 27
4.	545 + 10	22.	11,000 + 999
5.	1,532 + 10	23.	10,008 + 1,000
6.	1,745 + 10	24.	11,600 + 900
7.	2,321 + 10	25.	12,199 + 1,100
8.	2,499 + 100	26.	12,409 + 1,100
9.	2,678 + 100	27.	12,510 + 900
10.	3,129 + 100	28.	12,601 + 900
11.	4,209 + 100	29.	12,655 + 900
12.	4,399 + 100	30.	13,768 + 900
13.	3,576 + 1,000	31.	13,900 + 900
14.	4,748 + 1,000	32.	19,102 + 1,000
15.	5,552 + 1,000	33.	19,155 + 900
16.	6,799 + 1,000	34.	20,650 + 900
17.	7,490 + 1,100	35.	20,699 + 900
18.	7,750 + 1,100	36.	39,055 + 900

405 A Circle T for True or F for False. First Half

1.	2 is a factor of 4. T F	16.	36 is a factor of 6. T F
2.	2 is a factor of 8. T F	17.	6 is a factor of 48. T F
3.	8 is a multiple of 2. T F	18.	7 is a factor of 21. T F
4.	8 is a multiple of 4. T F	19.	7 is a multiple of 35. T F
5.	3 is a factor of 18. T F	20.	7 is a factor of 23. T F
6.	6 is a factor of 18. T F	21.	8 is a factor of 8. T F
7.	3 is a multiple of 6. T F	22.	8 is a multiple of 8. T F
8.	3 is a factor of 25. T F	23.	8 is a factor of 54. T F
9.	5 is a multiple of 5. T F	24.	8 is a multiple of 16. T F
10.	10 is a multiple of 5. T F	25.	8 is a factor of 24. T F
11.	10 is a multiple of 20. T F	26.	9 is a factor of 45. T F
12.	6 is a factor of 32. T F	27.	9 is a factor of 90. T F
13.	6 is a factor of 60. T F	28.	9 is a factor of 56. T F
14.	6 is a multiple of 12. T F	29.	9 is a multiple of 3. T F
15.	4 is a factor of 4. T F	30.	9 is a multiple of 9. T F

405 A | Circle T for True or F for False. | Second Half

1.	2 is a factor of 6.	T	F	16.	30 is a factor of 6.	T	F
2.	2 is a factor of 12.	T	F	17.	8 is a factor of 48.	T	F
3.	8 is a multiple of 4.	T	F	18.	7 is a factor of 14.	T	F
4.	8 is a multiple of 2.	T	F	19.	7 is a multiple of 35.	T	F
5.	3 is a factor of 15.	T	F	20.	7 is a factor of 33.	T	F
6.	6 is a factor of 12.	T	F	21.	6 is a factor of 6.	T	F
7.	3 is a multiple of 9.	T	F	22.	8 is a multiple of 8.	T	F
8.	3 is a factor of 26.	T	F	23.	8 is a factor of 54.	T	F
9.	7 is a multiple of 7.	T	F	24.	8 is a multiple of 16.	T	F
10.	20 is a multiple of 5.	T	F	25.	8 is a factor of 24.	T	F
11.	10 is a multiple of 30.	T	F	26.	9 is a factor of 45.	T	F
12.	6 is a factor of 52.	T	F	27.	9 is a factor of 90.	T	F
13.	7 is a factor of 70.	T	F	28.	9 is a factor of 56.	T	F
14.	7 is a multiple of 14.	T	F	29.	9 is a multiple of 3.	T	F
15.	7 is a factor of 7.	T	F	30.	9 is a multiple of 9.	T	F

405 B Circle T for True or F for False. First Half

1.	2 is a factor of 4.	T	F	16.	36 is a factor of 6.	T	F
2.	2 is a factor of 8.	T	F	17.	6 is a factor of 90.	T	F
3.	72 is a multiple of 3.	T	F	18.	7 is a factor of 91.	T	F
4.	92 is a multiple of 4.	T	F	19.	7 is a multiple of 35.	T	F
5.	3 is a factor of 102.	T	F	20.	7 is a factor of 99.	T	F
6.	6 is a factor of 126.	T	F	21.	8 is a factor of 8.	T	F
7.	3 is a multiple of 6.	T	F	22.	8 is a multiple of 8.	T	F
8.	3 is a factor of 62.	T	F	23.	8 is a factor of 108.	T	F
9.	5 is a multiple of 5.	T	F	24.	8 is a multiple of 16.	T	F
10.	10 is a multiple of 5.	T	F	25.	8 is a factor of 144.	T	F
11.	10 is a multiple of 20.	T	F	26.	9 is a factor of 234.	T	F
12.	6 is a factor of 86.	T	F	27.	9 is a factor of 189.	T	F
13.	6 is a factor of 234.	T	F	28.	9 is a factor of 323.	T	F
14.	6 is a multiple of 12.	T	F	29.	9 is a multiple of 3.	T	F
15.	4 is a factor of 4.	T	F	30.	9 is a multiple of 9.	T	F

405 B Circle T for True or F for False. Second Half

1.	2 is a factor of 8. T F		16.	42 is a factor of 6. T F
2.	2 is a factor of 10. T F		17.	6 is a factor of 90. T F
3.	69 is a multiple of 3. T F		18.	7 is a factor of 91. T F
4.	96 is a multiple of 4. T F		19.	7 is a multiple of 49. T F
5.	3 is a factor of 81. T F		20.	7 is a factor of 89. T F
6.	6 is a factor of 132. T F		21.	8 is a factor of 8. T F
7.	3 is a multiple of 9. T F		22.	8 is a multiple of 8. T F
8.	3 is a factor of 52. T F		23.	8 is a factor of 118. T F
9.	4 is a multiple of 4. T F		24.	8 is a multiple of 24. T F
10.	20 is a multiple of 5. T F		25.	8 is a factor of 144. T F
11.	10 is a multiple of 20. T F		26.	9 is a factor of 234. T F
12.	6 is a factor of 86. T F		27.	9 is a factor of 171. T F
13.	6 is a factor of 234. T F		28.	9 is a factor of 325. T F
14.	6 is a multiple of 12. T F		29.	9 is a multiple of 3. T F
15.	4 is a factor of 4. T F		30.	9 is a multiple of 9. T F

406 A — Circle T for True or F for False. — First Half

1.	3 is a factor of 9.	T F	13.	6 and 3 are factors of 12.	T F
2.	4 is a factor of 16.	T F	14.	24 and 32 are common factors of 8.	T F
3.	6 is a factor of 42.	T F	15.	3, 6, 9 and 18 are the only factors of 18.	T F
4.	6 is a factor of 6.	T F	16.	4 and 9 are common factors of 49.	T F
5.	6 is a factor of 3.	T F	17.	1 and 11 are all of the factors of 11.	T F
6.	8 is a factor of 2.	T F	18.	2 and 3 are factors of 66.	T F
7.	8 is a factor of 8.	T F	19.	3 and 4 are factors of 96.	T F
8.	2, 7 and 9 are factors of 56.	T F	20.	3 and 7 are factors of 84.	T F
9.	2, 3, 6 and 15 are factors of 30.	T F	21.	3 is a factor of 602.	T F
10.	4 and 8 are factors of 40.	T F	22.	9 is a factor of 108.	T F
11.	15 is a factor of 5.	T F	23.	9 is a factor of 333.	T F
12.	3, 6 and 8 are factors of 16.	T F	24.	9 is a factor of 7,011.	T F

406 A | Circle T for True or F for False. | Second Half

1.	3 is a factor of 6.	T F	13.	6 and 3 are factors of 18.	T F
2.	4 is a factor of 12.	T F	14.	24 and 32 are common factors of 4.	T F
3.	6 is a factor of 36.	T F	15.	3,4, 6 and 12 are the only factors of 12.	T F
4.	6 is a factor of 6.	T F	16.	3 and 6 are common factors of 63.	T F
5.	6 is a factor of 3.	T F	17.	1 and 13 are all of the factors of 13.	T F
6.	8 is a factor of 4.	T F	18.	2 and 3 are factors of 36.	T F
7.	8 is a factor of 8.	T F	19.	3 and 4 are factors of 96.	T F
8.	2, 7 and 9 are factors of 54.	T F	20.	3 and 7 are factors of 84.	T F
9.	2, 3, 6 and 15 are factors of 30.	T F	21.	3 is a factor of 602.	T F
10.	4 and 8 are factors of 80.	T F	22.	9 is a factor of 108.	T F
11.	15 is a factor of 3.	T F	23.	9 is a factor of 333.	T F
12.	3, 6 and 8 are factors of 18.	T F	24.	9 is a factor of 7,011.	T F

406 B — Circle T for True or F for False. — First Half

#	Statement		#	Statement	
1.	3 is a factor of 9.	T F	13.	6 and 3 are factors of 120.	T F
2.	4 is a factor of 48.	T F	14.	24 and 32 are common factors of 8.	T F
3.	6 is a factor of 72.	T F	15.	3,6,9 and 18 are the only factors of 18.	T F
4.	6 is a factor of 6.	T F	16.	4 and 9 are factors of 49.	T F
5.	600 is a factor of 150.	T F	17.	1 and 11 are all of the factors of 11.	T F
6.	8 is a factor of 2.	T F	18.	2 and 3 are factors of 132.	T F
7.	80 is a factor of 80.	T F	19.	3 and 4 are factors of 192.	T F
8.	2, 7 and 9 are factors of 56.	T F	20.	3 and 7 are factors of 336.	T F
9.	2, 3, 6 and 15 are factors of 30.	T F	21.	3 is a factor of 602.	T F
10.	4 and 8 are factors of 296.	T F	22.	9 is a factor of 2106.	T F
11.	15 is a factor of 5.	T F	23.	9 is a factor of 333.	T F
12.	3, 6 and 8 are factors of 160.	T F	24.	9 is a factor of 7,011.	T F

406 B Circle T for True or F for False. Second Half

1.	3 is a factor of 6.	T F	13.	6 and 3 are factors of 180.	T F
2.	4 is a factor of 24.	T F	14.	24 and 32 are common factors of 4.	T F
3.	6 is a factor of 54.	T F	15.	3,6,9 and 18 are the only factors of 18.	T F
4.	6 is a factor of 6.	T F	16.	4 and 9 are factors of 49.	T F
5.	450 is a factor of 150.	T F	17.	1 and 11 are all of the factors of 11.	T F
6.	8 is a factor of 4.	T F	18.	2 and 3 are factors of 132.	T F
7.	70 is a factor of 70.	T F	19.	3 and 4 are factors of 96.	T F
8.	2, 7 and 9 are factors of 54.	T F	20.	3 and 7 are factors of 672.	T F
9.	2, 3, 6 and 15 are factors of 60.	T F	21.	3 is a factor of 601.	T F
10.	4 and 8 are factors of 592.	T F	22.	9 is a factor of 3006.	T F
11.	20 is a factor of 5.	T F	23.	9 is a factor of 243.	T F
12.	3, 6 and 8 are factors of 150.	T F	24.	9 is a factor of 6,021.	T F

407 A | Add. | First Half

1.	10 + 10 =	16.	101 + 10 =
2.	10 + 9 =	17.	101 + 9 =
3.	9 + 10 =	18.	120 + 9 =
4.	11 + 10 =	19.	121 + 9 =
5.	11 + 9 =	20.	9 + 121 =
6.	21 + 9 =	21.	9 + 122 =
7.	31 + 9 =	22.	136 + 10 =
8.	9 + 41 =	23.	136 + 9 =
9.	8 + 41 =	24.	136 + 11 =
10.	51 + 10 =	25.	139 + 10 =
11.	51 + 11 =	26.	139 + 20 =
12.	59 + 10 =	27.	139 + 21 =
13.	59 + 9 =	28.	139 + 30 =
14.	59 + 11 =	29.	139 + 29 =
15.	69 + 9 =	30.	139 + 99 =

407 A | Add. | Second Half

1.	20 + 20 =	16.	100 + 10 =
2.	20 + 19 =	17.	100 + 9 =
3.	19 + 10 =	18.	110 + 9 =
4.	12 + 10 =	19.	111 + 9 =
5.	12 + 9 =	20.	9 + 111 =
6.	31 + 9 =	21.	9 + 112 =
7.	41 + 9 =	22.	146 + 10 =
8.	9 + 51 =	23.	146 + 9 =
9.	8 + 51 =	24.	146 + 11 =
10.	62 + 10 =	25.	149 + 10 =
11.	62 + 11 =	26.	149 + 20 =
12.	69 + 10 =	27.	149 + 21 =
13.	69 + 9 =	28.	159 + 30 =
14.	69 + 11 =	29.	159 + 29 =
15.	79 + 9 =	30.	159 + 99 =

407 B | Add or subtract. | First Half

1.	10 + 10 =	16.	51 + 50 + 10 =
2.	10 + 9 =	17.	51 + 50 + 9 =
3.	9 + 5 + 5 =	18.	80 + 9 + 40 =
4.	5 + 11 + 5 =	19.	61 + 60 + 9 =
5.	10 + 1 + 9 =	20.	9 + 71 + 50 =
6.	11 + 10 + 9 =	21.	9 + 61 + 61 =
7.	21 + 9 + 10 =	22.	136 + 10 =
8.	9 + 41 =	23.	136 + 9 =
9.	8 + 21 + 20 =	24.	136 + 11 =
10.	31 + 10 + 20 =	25.	127 + 10 + 12 =
11.	21 + 11 + 30 =	26.	200 – 41 =
12.	29 + 30 + 10 =	27.	201 – 41 =
13.	59 + 9 =	28.	209 – 40 =
14.	59 + 11 =	29.	139 + 29 =
15.	32 + 37 + 9 =	30.	139 + 99 =

407 B | Add or subtract. | Second Half

1.	20 + 20 =	16.	50 + 50 + 10 =
2.	20 + 19 =	17.	50 + 50 + 9 =
3.	19 + 5 + 5 =	18.	80 + 9 + 30 =
4.	5 + 12 + 5 =	19.	61 + 50 + 9 =
5.	3 + 9 + 9 =	20.	9 + 61 + 50 =
6.	21 + 10 + 9 =	21.	9 + 51 + 61 =
7.	31 + 9 + 10 =	22.	146 + 10 =
8.	9 + 51 =	23.	146 + 9 =
9.	8 + 31 + 20 =	24.	146 + 11 =
10.	32 + 10 + 30 =	25.	127 + 10 + 22 =
11.	32 + 11 + 30 =	26.	200 – 31 =
12.	39 + 30 + 10 =	27.	201 – 31 =
13.	69 + 9 =	28.	209 – 20 =
14.	59 + 11 + 10 =	29.	159 + 29 =
15.	42 + 37 + 9 =	30.	159 + 99 =

408 A | Subtract. | First Half

1.	10 – 10 =	16.	120 – 10 =
2.	20 – 10 =	17.	120 – 20 =
3.	30 – 10 =	18.	130 – 20 =
4.	50 – 10 =	19.	130 – 19 =
5.	50 – 9 =	20.	140 – 20 =
6.	60 – 9 =	21.	140 – 21 =
7.	90 – 9 =	22.	160 – 30 =
8.	100 – 9 =	23.	160 – 40 =
9.	101 – 10 =	24.	160 – 39 =
10.	101 – 9 =	25.	160 – 29 =
11.	101 – 11 =	26.	160 – 19 =
12.	103 – 9 =	27.	160 – 9 =
13.	119 – 10 =	28.	160 – 10 =
14.	119 – 9 =	29.	160 – 11 =
15.	119 – 11 =	30.	160 – 99 =

408 A | Subtract. | Second Half

1.	20 – 20 =	16.	110 – 10 =
2.	30 – 10 =	17.	110 – 20 =
3.	40 – 10 =	18.	110 – 30 =
4.	60 – 10 =	19.	110 – 19 =
5.	60 – 9 =	20.	120 – 20 =
6.	70 – 9 =	21.	120 – 21 =
7.	80 – 9 =	22.	140 – 30 =
8.	100 – 9 =	23.	140 – 40 =
9.	101 – 10 =	24.	140 – 39 =
10.	101 – 9 =	25.	140 – 29 =
11.	101 – 11 =	26.	140 – 19 =
12.	102 – 9 =	27.	140 – 9 =
13.	112 – 10 =	28.	150 – 10 =
14.	112 – 9 =	29.	150 – 11 =
15.	112 – 11 =	30.	150 – 99 =

408 B | Subtract. | First Half

1.	110 – 110 =	16.	420 – 310 =
2.	120 – 110 =	17.	420 – 320 =
3.	130 – 110 =	18.	430 – 320 =
4.	250 – 210 =	19.	430 – 319 =
5.	250 – 209 =	20.	540 – 420 =
6.	260 – 209 =	21.	640 – 521 =
7.	390 – 309 =	22.	760 – 630 =
8.	100 – 9 =	23.	760 – 640 =
9.	101 – 10 =	24.	360 – 239 =
10.	201 – 109 =	25.	360 – 229 =
11.	201 – 111 =	26.	360 – 219 =
12.	203 – 109 =	27.	360 – 209 =
13.	319 – 210 =	28.	460 – 310 =
14.	319 – 209 =	29.	460 – 311 =
15.	319 – 211 =	30.	160 – 99 =

408 B | Subtract. | Second Half

1.	120 – 120 =	16.	420 – 320 =
2.	130 – 110 =	17.	420 – 330 =
3.	140 – 110 =	18.	430 – 350 =
4.	260 – 210 =	19.	400 – 309 =
5.	260 – 209 =	20.	540 – 440 =
6.	270 – 209 =	21.	640 – 541 =
7.	280 – 209 =	22.	760 – 650 =
8.	200 – 109 =	23.	760 – 660 =
9.	201 – 110 =	24.	360 – 259 =
10.	201 – 109 =	25.	360 – 249 =
11.	201 – 111 =	26.	360 – 239 =
12.	202 – 109 =	27.	360 – 229 =
13.	312 – 210 =	28.	460 – 320 =
14.	312 – 209 =	29.	460 – 321 =
15.	312 – 211 =	30.	150 – 99 =

409 A | Add or subtract. | First Half

1.	50 + 50 =	16.	245 + 155 =
2.	100 – 50 =	17.	400 – 155 =
3.	60 + 60 =	18.	500 – 255 =
4.	120 – 60 =	19.	175 + 25 =
5.	65 + 65 =	20.	200 – 25 =
6.	75 + 65 =	21.	200 – 35 =
7.	65 + 70 =	22.	210 – 25 =
8.	135 – 65 =	23.	210 – 35 =
9.	135 – 70 =	24.	210 – 55 =
10.	200 – 10 =	25.	210 – 60 =
11.	200 – 20 =	26.	210 – 65 =
12.	200 – 25 =	27.	220 – 60 =
13.	200 – 35 =	28.	220 – 65 =
14.	200 – 45 =	29.	135 + 65 =
15.	145 + 155 =	30.	135 + 175 =

409 A Add or subtract. Second Half

1.	40 + 40 =	16.	255 + 155 =
2.	80 – 40 =	17.	300 – 155 =
3.	30 + 30 =	18.	400 – 255 =
4.	60 – 30 =	19.	195 + 5 =
5.	45 + 45 =	20.	200 – 5 =
6.	55 + 55 =	21.	200 – 15 =
7.	55 + 60 =	22.	210 – 15 =
8.	115 – 55 =	23.	210 – 25 =
9.	115 – 60 =	24.	210 – 35 =
10.	300 – 20 =	25.	220 – 40 =
11.	300 – 30 =	26.	210 – 45 =
12.	300 – 25 =	27.	220 – 50 =
13.	300 – 35 =	28.	220 – 55 =
14.	300 – 45 =	29.	165 + 35 =
15.	245 + 155 =	30.	135 + 175 =

409 B	Add or subtract.		First Half
1.	50 + 50 =	16.	245 + 125 + 30 =
2.	100 – 50 =	17.	400 – 155 =
3.	60 + 30 + 30 =	18.	500 – 255 =
4.	120 – 60 =	19.	165 + 25 + 10 =
5.	65 + 35 + 30 =	20.	300 – 125 =
6.	75 + 15 + 50 =	21.	300 – 135 =
7.	65 + 40 + 30 =	22.	310 – 125 =
8.	235 – 165 =	23.	310 – 135 =
9.	235 – 170 =	24.	310 – 155 =
10.	200 – 10 =	25.	310 – 160 =
11.	200 – 20 =	26.	310 – 165 =
12.	300 – 125 =	27.	320 – 160 =
13.	300 – 135 =	28.	320 – 165 =
14.	300 – 145 =	29.	135 + 65 =
15.	145 + 155 =	30.	135 + 175 =

409 B | Add or subtract. | Second Half

1.	40 + 40 =	16.	145 + 155 + 110 =
2.	80 – 40 =	17.	400 – 255 =
3.	20 + 20 + 20 =	18.	500 – 355 =
4.	120 – 90 =	19.	165 + 25 + 10 =
5.	25 + 35 + 30 =	20.	300 – 105 =
6.	75 + 15 + 20 =	21.	300 – 115 =
7.	65 + 10 + 40 =	22.	310 – 115 =
8.	235 – 175 =	23.	310 – 125 =
9.	235 – 180 =	24.	310 – 135 =
10.	500 – 220 =	25.	320 – 140 =
11.	500 – 230 =	26.	310 – 145 =
12.	400 – 125 =	27.	320 – 150 =
13.	400 – 135 =	28.	320 – 155 =
14.	400 – 145 =	29.	135 + 65 =
15.	245 + 155 =	30.	135 + 175 =

410 A | Multiply. | First Half

1.	2 x 3 =	16.	5 x 4 =
2.	2 x 6 =	17.	5 x 6 =
3.	2 x 12 =	18.	6 x 5 =
4.	3 x 3 =	19.	7 x 5 =
5.	3 x 6 =	20.	9 x 5 =
6.	3 x 9 =	21.	5 x 12 =
7.	3 x 12 =	22.	5 x 13 =
8.	4 x 4 =	23.	5 x 11 =
9.	4 x 8 =	24.	4 x 11 =
10.	4 x 12 =	25.	4 x 9 =
11.	4 x 13 =	26.	4 x 8 =
12.	4 x 14 =	27.	4 x 6 =
13.	4 x 10 =	28.	4 x 7 =
14.	4 x 20 =	29.	4 x 12 =
15.	5 x 2 =	30.	13 x 4 =

410 A | Multiply. | Second Half

1.	2 x 2 =	16.	5 x 3 =
2.	2 x 4 =	17.	5 x 4 =
3.	2 x 8 =	18.	6 x 5 =
4.	3 x 2 =	19.	7 x 5 =
5.	3 x 4 =	20.	9 x 5 =
6.	3 x 8 =	21.	5 x 11 =
7.	3 x 10 =	22.	5 x 12 =
8.	4 x 3 =	23.	5 x 13 =
9.	4 x 6 =	24.	4 x 10 =
10.	4 x 9 =	25.	4 x 8 =
11.	4 x 12 =	26.	4 x 7 =
12.	4 x 13 =	27.	4 x 6 =
13.	4 x 10 =	28.	4 x 4 =
14.	4 x 20 =	29.	4 x 12 =
15.	5 x 2 =	30.	13 x 4 =

410 B | Divide. | First Half

1.	$12 \div 2 =$	16.	$40 \div 2 =$
2.	$24 \div 2 =$	17.	$60 \div 2 =$
3.	$48 \div 2 =$	18.	$90 \div 3 =$
4.	$18 \div 2 =$	19.	$105 \div 3 =$
5.	$36 \div 2 =$	20.	$135 \div 3 =$
6.	$54 \div 2 =$	21.	$240 \div 4 =$
7.	$72 \div 2 =$	22.	$195 \div 3 =$
8.	$48 \div 3 =$	23.	$165 \div 3 =$
9.	$64 \div 2 =$	24.	$132 \div 3 =$
10.	$96 \div 2 =$	25.	$108 \div 3 =$
11.	$104 \div 2 =$	26.	$96 \div 3 =$
12.	$112 \div 2 =$	27.	$96 \div 4 =$
13.	$120 \div 3 =$	28.	$84 \div 3 =$
14.	$160 \div 2 =$	29.	$48 \div 1 =$
15.	$60 \div 6 =$	30.	$104 \div 2$

410 B | Divide. | Second Half

1.	$12 \div 3 =$	16.	$30 \div 2 =$
2.	$16 \div 2 =$	17.	$40 \div 2 =$
3.	$32 \div 2 =$	18.	$90 \div 3 =$
4.	$12 \div 2 =$	19.	$105 \div 3 =$
5.	$24 \div 2 =$	20.	$135 \div 3 =$
6.	$48 \div 2 =$	21.	$165 \div 3 =$
7.	$60 \div 2 =$	22.	$180 \div 3 =$
8.	$36 \div 3 =$	23.	$195 \div 3 =$
9.	$48 \div 2 =$	24.	$160 \div 4 =$
10.	$72 \div 2 =$	25.	$96 \div 3 =$
11.	$96 \div 2 =$	26.	$56 \div 2 =$
12.	$104 \div 2 =$	27.	$96 \div 4 =$
13.	$120 \div 3 =$	28.	$48 \div 3 =$
14.	$160 \div 2 =$	29.	$48 \div 1 =$
15.	$60 \div 6 =$	30.	$104 \div 2 =$

411 A | Divide. | First Half

1.	$4 \div 2 =$	16.	$10 \div 5 =$
2.	$6 \div 2 =$	17.	$20 \div 5 =$
3.	$12 \div 2 =$	18.	$40 \div 5 =$
4.	$24 \div 2 =$	19.	$60 \div 5 =$
5.	$9 \div 3 =$	20.	$35 \div 5 =$
6.	$15 \div 3 =$	21.	$45 \div 5 =$
7.	$21 \div 3 =$	22.	$30 \div 3 =$
8.	$24 \div 3 =$	23.	$40 \div 4 =$
9.	$27 \div 3 =$	24.	$50 \div 5 =$
10.	$33 \div 3 =$	25.	$33 \div 3 =$
11.	$12 \div 4 =$	26.	$36 \div 3 =$
12.	$20 \div 4 =$	27.	$39 \div 3 =$
13.	$32 \div 4 =$	28.	$40 \div 4 =$
14.	$36 \div 4 =$	29.	$48 \div 4 =$
15.	$44 \div 4 =$	30.	$52 \div 4 =$

411 A | Divide. | Second Half

1.	$6 \div 2 =$	16.	$5 \div 5 =$
2.	$8 \div 2 =$	17.	$10 \div 5 =$
3.	$14 \div 2 =$	18.	$20 \div 5 =$
4.	$20 \div 2 =$	19.	$15 \div 5 =$
5.	$6 \div 3 =$	20.	$30 \div 5 =$
6.	$9 \div 3 =$	21.	$40 \div 5 =$
7.	$12 \div 3 =$	22.	$30 \div 3 =$
8.	$18 \div 3 =$	23.	$40 \div 4 =$
9.	$21 \div 3 =$	24.	$50 \div 5 =$
10.	$27 \div 3 =$	25.	$33 \div 3 =$
11.	$8 \div 4 =$	26.	$36 \div 3 =$
12.	$16 \div 4 =$	27.	$39 \div 3 =$
13.	$24 \div 4 =$	28.	$42 \div 3 =$
14.	$28 \div 4 =$	29.	$45 \div 3 =$
15.	$32 \div 4 =$	30.	$51 \div 3 =$

411 B Divide. First Half

1.	4 ÷ 2 =	16.	100 ÷ 50 =
2.	6 ÷ 2 =	17.	76 ÷ 19 =
3.	120 ÷ 20 =	18.	200 ÷ 25 =
4.	240 ÷ 20 =	19.	384 ÷ 32 =
5.	90 ÷ 30 =	20.	203 ÷ 29 =
6.	150 ÷ 30 =	21.	450 ÷ 50 =
7.	210 ÷ 30 =	22.	300 ÷ 30 =
8.	240 ÷ 30 =	23.	400 ÷ 40 =
9.	270 ÷ 30 =	24.	500 ÷ 50 =
10.	330 ÷ 30 =	25.	330 ÷ 30 =
11.	120 ÷ 40 =	26.	360 ÷ 30 =
12.	200 ÷ 40 =	27.	390 ÷ 30 =
13.	320 ÷ 40 =	28.	400 ÷ 40 =
14.	360 ÷ 40 =	29.	480 ÷ 40 =
15.	440 ÷ 40 =	30.	520 ÷ 40 =

411 B Divide. Second Half

1.	$6 \div 2 =$	16.	$100 \div 100 =$
2.	$8 \div 2 =$	17.	$38 \div 19 =$
3.	$140 \div 20 =$	18.	$220 \div 55 =$
4.	$200 \div 20 =$	19.	$96 \div 32 =$
5.	$60 \div 30 =$	20.	$174 \div 29 =$
6.	$150 \div 50 =$	21.	$400 \div 50 =$
7.	$120 \div 30 =$	22.	$310 \div 31 =$
8.	$180 \div 30 =$	23.	$410 \div 41 =$
9.	$210 \div 30 =$	24.	$510 \div 51 =$
10.	$270 \div 30 =$	25.	$440 \div 40 =$
11.	$120 \div 60 =$	26.	$360 \div 30 =$
12.	$200 \div 50 =$	27.	$390 \div 30 =$
13.	$360 \div 60 =$	28.	$420 \div 30 =$
14.	$280 \div 40 =$	29.	$450 \div 30 =$
15.	$320 \div 40 =$	30.	$510 \div 30 =$

412 A | Multiply or divide. | First Half

1.	$6 \times 1 =$	16.	$4 \times 7 =$
2.	$6 \times 2 =$	17.	$7 \times 6 =$
3.	$3 \times 6 =$	18.	$7 \times 7 =$
4.	$4 \times 6 =$	19.	$7 \times 9 =$
5.	$6 \times 6 =$	20.	$7 \times 8 =$
6.	$7 \times 6 =$	21.	$7 \times 10 =$
7.	$6 \times 9 =$	22.	$56 \div 7 =$
8.	$8 \times 6 =$	23.	$63 \div 7 =$
9.	$12 \div 6 =$	24.	$42 \div 7 =$
10.	$24 \div 6 =$	25.	$8 \times 2 =$
11.	$48 \div 6 =$	26.	$4 \times 8 =$
12.	$36 \div 6 =$	27.	$8 \times 6 =$
13.	$42 \div 6 =$	28.	$7 \times 8 =$
14.	$54 \div 6 =$	29.	$9 \times 8 =$
15.	$7 \times 2 =$	30.	$8 \times 8 =$

412 A | Multiply or divide. | Second Half

1.	6 x 2 =	16.	5 x 7 =
2.	6 x 3 =	17.	7 x 4 =
3.	5 x 6 =	18.	6 x 7 =
4.	4 x 6 =	19.	7 x 8 =
5.	6 x 6 =	20.	7 x 7 =
6.	8 x 6 =	21.	7 x 9 =
7.	6 x 9 =	22.	63 ÷ 7 =
8.	11 x 6 =	23.	70 ÷ 7 =
9.	12 ÷ 6 =	24.	49 ÷ 7 =
10.	18 ÷ 6 =	25.	8 x 2 =
11.	36 ÷ 6 =	26.	5 x 8 =
12.	42 ÷ 6 =	27.	8 x 3 =
13.	30 ÷ 6 =	28.	7 x 8 =
14.	54 ÷ 6 =	29.	9 x 8 =
15.	7 x 3 =	30.	8 x 8 =

412 B | Multiply or divide. | First Half

1.	12 ÷ 2 =	16.	2 x 7 x 2 =
2.	36 ÷ 3 =	17.	2 x 7 x 3 =
3.	36 ÷ 2 =	18.	7 x 7 =
4.	48 ÷ 2 =	19.	7 x 3 x 3 =
5.	72 ÷ 2 =	20.	2 x 7 x 4 =
6.	7 x 6 =	21.	5 x 7 x 2 =
7.	6 x 9 =	22.	56 ÷ 7 =
8.	2 x 6 x 4 =	23.	63 ÷ 7 =
9.	96 ÷ 48 =	24.	420 ÷ 70 =
10.	32 ÷ 8 =	25.	2 x 2 x 2 x 2 =
11.	48 ÷ 6 =	26.	320 ÷ 10 =
12.	36 ÷ 6 =	27.	2 x 4 x 2 x 3 =
13.	42 ÷ 6 =	28.	4 x 7 x 2 =
14.	108 ÷ 12 =	29.	3 x 8 x 3 =
15.	42 ÷ 3 =	30.	8 x 8 =

412 B | Multiply or divide. | Second Half

1.	24 ÷ 2 =	16.	5 x 7 =
2.	3 x 3 x 2 =	17.	2 x 7 x 2 =
3.	60 ÷ 2 =	18.	2 x 7 x 3 =
4.	48 ÷ 2 =	19.	7 x 2 x 4 =
5.	72 ÷ 2 =	20.	7 x 7 =
6.	8 x 6 =	21.	3 x 7 x 3
7.	6 x 9 =	22.	63 ÷ 7 =
8.	2 x 11 x 3 =	23.	630 ÷ 63 =
9.	84 ÷ 42 =	24.	490 ÷ 70 =
10.	24 ÷ 8 =	25.	2 x 2 x 2 x 2 =
11.	36 ÷ 6 =	26.	440 ÷ 11 =
12.	210 ÷ 30 =	27.	2 x 4 x 3 =
13.	350 ÷ 70 =	28.	4 x 7 x 2 =
14.	108 ÷ 12 =	29.	3 x 8 x 3 =
15.	63 ÷ 3 =	30.	128 ÷ 2 =

413 A | Multiply or divide. | First Half

1.	8 x 2 =	16.	16 ÷ 8 =
2.	9 x 2 =	17.	24 ÷ 8 =
3.	8 x 3 =	18.	32 ÷ 8 =
4.	9 x 3 =	19.	40 ÷ 8 =
5.	8 x 4 =	20.	48 ÷ 8 =
6.	9 x 4 =	21.	64 ÷ 8 =
7.	8 x 6 =	22.	56 ÷ 8 =
8.	9 x 6 =	23.	18 ÷ 2 =
9.	8 x 7 =	24.	36 ÷ 9 =
10.	7 x 8 =	25.	45 ÷ 9 =
11.	7 x 9 =	26.	54 ÷ 9 =
12.	8 x 5 =	27.	72 ÷ 9 =
13.	8 x 6 =	28.	90 ÷ 9 =
14.	8 x 8 =	29.	81 ÷ 9 =
15.	8 x 10 =	30.	99 ÷ 9 =

413 A | Multiply or divide. | Second Half

1.	8 x 1 =	16.	16 ÷ 8 =
2.	8 x 2 =	17.	24 ÷ 8 =
3.	9 x 2 =	18.	32 ÷ 8 =
4.	9 x 3 =	19.	40 ÷ 8 =
5.	8 x 5 =	20.	48 ÷ 8 =
6.	9 x 5 =	21.	72 ÷ 8 =
7.	8 x 4 =	22.	64 ÷ 8 =
8.	9 x 4 =	23.	56 ÷ 8 =
9.	8 x 6 =	24.	27 ÷ 9 =
10.	6 x 8 =	25.	54 ÷ 9 =
11.	7 x 9 =	26.	72 ÷ 9 =
12.	8 x 5 =	27.	63 ÷ 9 =
13.	8 x 6 =	28.	90 ÷ 9 =
14.	8 x 8 =	29.	81 ÷ 9 =
15.	8 x 10 =	30.	99 ÷ 9 =

413 B | Multiply or divide. | First Half

1.	8 x 2 =	16.	160 ÷ 80 =
2.	9 x 2 =	17.	240 ÷ 80 =
3.	8 x 3 =	18.	320 ÷ 80 =
4.	9 x 3 =	19.	400 ÷ 80 =
5.	2 x 4 x 4 =	20.	480 ÷ 80 =
6.	3 x 3 x 4 =	21.	640 ÷ 80 =
7.	8 x 3 x 2 =	22.	560 ÷ 80 =
8.	9 x 3 x 2 =	23.	189 ÷ 21 =
9.	2 x 4 x 7 =	24.	156 ÷ 39 =
10.	7 x 8 =	25.	450 ÷ 90 =
11.	7 x 9 =	26.	54 ÷ 9 =
12.	2 x 2 x 2 x 5 =	27.	720 ÷ 90 =
13.	8 x 6 =	28.	900 ÷ 90 =
14.	8 x 8 =	29.	810 ÷ 90 =
15.	160 ÷ 2 =	30.	990 ÷ 90 =

413 B | Multiply or divide. | Second Half

1.	4 x 2 x 1 =	16.	160 ÷ 80 =
2.	2 x 2 x 2 x 2 =	17.	240 ÷ 80 =
3.	2 x 3 x 3 =	18.	320 ÷ 80 =
4.	9 x 3 =	19.	400 ÷ 80 =
5.	5 x 4 x 2 =	20.	480 ÷ 80 =
6.	3 x 3 x 5 =	21.	720 ÷ 80 =
7.	8 x 2 x 2 =	22.	168 ÷ 21 =
8.	9 x 2 x 2 =	23.	203 ÷ 29 =
9.	2 x 4 x 6 =	24.	102 ÷ 34 =
10.	6 x 8 =	25.	120 ÷ 20 =
11.	7 x 9 =	26.	72 ÷ 9 =
12.	2 x 2 x 2 x 5 =	27.	630 ÷ 90 =
13.	8 x 6 =	28.	900 ÷ 90 =
14.	8 x 8 =	29.	810 ÷ 90 =
15.	160 ÷ 2 =	30.	1,100 ÷ 100 =

414 A | Multiply or divide. | First Half

1.	3 x 3 =	16.	9 ÷ 3 =
2.	3 x 6 =	17.	18 ÷ 3 =
3.	3 x 8 =	18.	24 ÷ 3 =
4.	4 x 3 =	19.	12 ÷ 4 =
5.	4 x 6 =	20.	24 ÷ 4 =
6.	4 x 8 =	21.	36 ÷ 4 =
7.	4 x 9 =	22.	18 ÷ 6 =
8.	6 x 3 =	23.	24 ÷ 6 =
9.	6 x 5 =	24.	36 ÷ 6 =
10.	6 x 6 =	25.	48 ÷ 6 =
11.	6 x 8 =	26.	54 ÷ 9 =
12.	7 x 6 =	27.	72 ÷ 9 =
13.	7 x 7 =	28.	63 ÷ 9 =
14.	7 x 8 =	29.	45 ÷ 9 =
15.	7 x 9 =	30.	108 ÷ 9 =

414 A | Multiply or divide. | Second Half

1.	3 x 2 =	16.	12 ÷ 3 =
2.	3 x 4 =	17.	21 ÷ 3 =
3.	3 x 6 =	18.	15 ÷ 3 =
4.	4 x 8 =	19.	12 ÷ 4 =
5.	4 x 2 =	20.	24 ÷ 4 =
6.	4 x 4 =	21.	36 ÷ 4 =
7.	4 x 6 =	22.	18 ÷ 6 =
8.	6 x 2 =	23.	24 ÷ 6 =
9.	6 x 3 =	24.	36 ÷ 6 =
10.	6 x 4 =	25.	48 ÷ 6 =
11.	6 x 6 =	26.	54 ÷ 9 =
12.	7 x 6 =	27.	72 ÷ 9 =
13.	7 x 7 =	28.	63 ÷ 9 =
14.	7 x 11 =	29.	45 ÷ 9 =
15.	7 x 10 =	30.	108 ÷ 9 =

414 B | Multiply or divide. | First Half

1.	3 x 3 =	16.	99 ÷ 33 =
2.	3 x 2 x 3 =	17.	180 ÷ 30 =
3.	3 x 4 x 2 =	18.	120 ÷ 15 =
4.	2 x 3 x 2 =	19.	120 ÷ 40 =
5.	48 ÷ 2 =	20.	240 ÷ 40 =
6.	4 x 8 =	21.	189 ÷ 21 =
7.	72 ÷ 2 =	22.	180 ÷ 60 =
8.	36 ÷ 2 =	23.	88 ÷ 22 =
9.	2 x 5 x 3 =	24.	36 ÷ 6 =
10.	2 x 3 x 6 =	25.	48 ÷ 6 =
11.	6 x 2 x 2 x 2 =	26.	540 ÷ 90 =
12.	7 x 3 x 2 =	27.	72 ÷ 9 =
13.	7 x 7 =	28.	630 ÷ 90 =
14.	7 x 8 =	29.	45 ÷ 9 =
15.	7 x 9 =	30.	108 ÷ 9 =

Math Sprints 4

414 B | Multiply or divide. | Second Half

1.	3 x 2 =	16.	96 ÷ 24 =
2.	3 x 2 x 2=	17.	210 ÷ 30 =
3.	3 x 3 x 2 =	18.	120 ÷ 24 =
4.	2 x 8 x 2 =	19.	120 ÷ 40 =
5.	48 ÷ 6 =	20.	240 ÷ 40 =
6.	4 x 2 x 2 =	21.	189 ÷ 21 =
7.	72 ÷ 3 =	22.	180 ÷ 60 =
8.	36 ÷ 3 =	23.	88 ÷ 22 =
9.	2 x 3 x 3 =	24.	36 ÷ 6 =
10.	2 x 3 x 4 =	25.	48 ÷ 6 =
11.	6 x 2 x 3 =	26.	540 ÷ 90 =
12.	7 x 3 x 2 =	27.	72 ÷ 9 =
13.	7 x 7 =	28.	630 ÷ 90 =
14.	7 x 11 =	29.	45 ÷ 9 =
15.	7 x 5 x 2 =	30.	108 ÷ 9 =

415 A | Multiply. | First Half

1.	6 x 10 =	16.	60 x 10 =
2.	10 x 10 =	17.	60 x 20 =
3.	16 x 10 =	18.	60 x 3 =
4.	8 x 10 =	19.	12 x 3 x 5 x 10 =
5.	10 x 10 =	20.	40 x 5 =
6.	18 x 10 =	21.	40 x 10 =
7.	19 x 10 =	22.	40 x 15 =
8.	20 x 10 =	23.	40 x 20 =
9.	20 x 20 =	24.	40 x 30 =
10.	14 x 10 =	25.	42 x 10 =
11.	14 x 20 =	26.	42 x 5 =
12.	14 x 30 =	27.	42 x 15 =
13.	14 x 40 =	28.	54 x 10 =
14.	40 x 7 =	29.	9 x 5 x 6 =
15.	40 x 70 =	30.	54 x 15 =

415 A Multiply. Second Half

1.	7 x 10 =	16.	70 x 10 =
2.	10 x 10 =	17.	70 x 20 =
3.	17 x 10 =	18.	70 x 3 =
4.	9 x 10 =	19.	70 x 30 =
5.	10 x 10 =	20.	80 x 5 =
6.	19 x 10 =	21.	80 x 10 =
7.	18 x 10 =	22.	80 x 15 =
8.	30 x 10 =	23.	40 x 20 =
9.	30 x 20 =	24.	40 x 30 =
10.	16 x 10 =	25.	42 x 10 =
11.	16 x 20 =	26.	42 x 5 =
12.	16 x 30 =	27.	42 x 15 =
13.	16 x 40 =	28.	54 x 10 =
14.	40 x 7 =	29.	9 x 5 x 6 =
15.	40 x 70 =	30.	54 x 15 =

415 B | Multiply. | First Half

1.	6 x 10 =	16.	60 x 2 x 5 =
2.	10 x 10 =	17.	60 x 4 x 5 =
3.	16 x 10 =	18.	6 x 10 x 3 =
4.	4 x 2 x 10 =	19.	60 x 30 =
5.	5 x 2 x 10 =	20.	8 x 5 x 5 =
6.	18 x 10 =	21.	40 x 10 =
7.	19 x 10 =	22.	40 x 15 =
8.	20 x 2 x 5 =	23.	8 x 5 x 20 =
9.	20 x 20 =	24.	40 x 3 x 10 =
10.	14 x 10 =	25.	42 x 10 =
11.	14 x 20 =	26.	42 x 5 =
12.	14 x 3 x 10 =	27.	42 x 15 =
13.	7 x 2 x 40 =	28.	54 x 10 =
14.	40 x 7 =	29.	54 x 5 =
15.	40 x 70 =	30.	54 x 15 =

415 B Multiply. Second Half

1.	7 x 10 =	16.	70 x 10 =
2.	10 x 10 =	17.	70 x 20 =
3.	17 x 10 =	18.	7 x 10 x 3 =
4.	9 x 10 =	19.	70 x 30 =
5.	5 x 2 x 10 =	20.	8 x 10 x 5 =
6.	19 x 10 =	21.	80 x 10 =
7.	18 x 10 =	22.	80 x 15 =
8.	30 x 2 x 5 =	23.	8 x 5 x 20 =
9.	30 x 20 =	24.	40 x 3 x 10 =
10.	16 x 10 =	25.	42 x 10 =
11.	16 x 20 =	26.	42 x 5 =
12.	16 x 3 x 10 =	27.	42 x 15 =
13.	8 x 2 x 40 =	28.	54 x 10 =
14.	40 x 7 =	29.	54 x 5 =
15.	40 x 70 =	30.	54 x 15 =

416 A — Divide. — First Half

1.	80 ÷ 1 =	11.	600 ÷ 10 =
2.	80 ÷ 10 =	12.	30 ÷ 10 =
3.	800 ÷ 10 =	13.	630 ÷ 10 =
4.	8,000 ÷ 10 =	14.	6,300 ÷ 10 =
5.	800 ÷ 100 =	15.	6,300 ÷ 100 =
6.	8,000 ÷ 100 =	16.	700 ÷ 10 =
7.	840 ÷ 1 =	17.	20 ÷ 10 =
8.	840 ÷ 10 =	18.	720 ÷ 10 =
9.	8,400 ÷ 10 =	19.	720 ÷ 20 =
10.	8,400 ÷ 100 =	20.	720 ÷ 72 =

416 A Divide. Second Half

1.	$70 \div 1 =$	11.	$500 \div 10 =$
2.	$70 \div 10 =$	12.	$50 \div 10 =$
3.	$700 \div 10 =$	13.	$560 \div 10 =$
4.	$7{,}000 \div 10 =$	14.	$5{,}600 \div 10 =$
5.	$700 \div 100 =$	15.	$5{,}600 \div 100 =$
6.	$7{,}000 \div 100 =$	16.	$700 \div 10 =$
7.	$720 \div 1 =$	17.	$20 \div 10 =$
8.	$720 \div 10 =$	18.	$720 \div 10 =$
9.	$7{,}200 \div 10 =$	19.	$720 \div 20 =$
10.	$7{,}200 \div 100 =$	20.	$720 \div 72 =$

416 B | Divide. | First Half

1.	$80 \div 1 =$	11.	$1{,}200 \div 20 =$
2.	$80 \div 10 =$	12.	$330 \div 110 =$
3.	$800 \div 10 =$	13.	$693 \div 11 =$
4.	$9{,}600 \div 12 =$	14.	$6{,}300 \div 10 =$
5.	$880 \div 110 =$	15.	$756 \div 12 =$
6.	$8{,}000 \div 100 =$	16.	$700 \div 10 =$
7.	$8{,}400 \div 10 =$	17.	$20 \div 10 =$
8.	$840 \div 10 =$	18.	$720 \div 10 =$
9.	$16{,}800 \div 20 =$	19.	$720 \div 20 =$
10.	$8{,}400 \div 100 =$	20.	$720 \div 72 =$

416 B | Divide. | Second Half

1.	70 ÷ 1 =	11.	3,000 ÷ 60 =
2.	70 ÷ 10 =	12.	550 ÷ 110 =
3.	700 ÷ 10 =	13.	1,680 ÷ 30 =
4.	8,400 ÷ 12 =	14.	5,600 ÷ 10 =
5.	770 ÷ 110 =	15.	672 ÷ 12 =
6.	7,000 ÷ 100 =	16.	700 ÷ 10 =
7.	7,200 ÷ 10 =	17.	20 ÷ 10 =
8.	720 ÷ 10 =	18.	720 ÷ 10 =
9.	14,400 ÷ 20 =	19.	720 ÷ 20 =
10.	7,200 ÷ 100 =	20.	720 ÷ 72 =

417 A | Fill in the missing part of the fraction. | First Half

1.	$\frac{1}{2} = \frac{\quad}{4}$	13.	$\frac{3}{7} = \frac{\quad}{42}$
2.	$\frac{1}{3} = \frac{\quad}{6}$	14.	$\frac{4}{7} = \frac{16}{\quad}$
3.	$\frac{1}{4} = \frac{\quad}{8}$	15.	$\frac{5}{7} = \frac{\quad}{49}$
4.	$\frac{1}{5} = \frac{\quad}{15}$	16.	$\frac{1}{8} = \frac{\quad}{64}$
5.	$\frac{1}{6} = \frac{\quad}{18}$	17.	$\frac{3}{8} = \frac{15}{\quad}$
6.	$\frac{2}{3} = \frac{6}{\quad}$	18.	$\frac{5}{8} = \frac{\quad}{72}$
7.	$\frac{3}{4} = \frac{9}{\quad}$	19.	$\frac{7}{8} = \frac{56}{\quad}$
8.	$\frac{2}{10} = \frac{6}{\quad}$	20.	$\frac{1}{9} = \frac{5}{\quad}$
9.	$\frac{3}{10} = \frac{\quad}{40}$	21.	$\frac{2}{9} = \frac{\quad}{36}$
10.	$\frac{3}{5} = \frac{15}{\quad}$	22.	$\frac{5}{9} = \frac{\quad}{72}$
11.	$\frac{5}{6} = \frac{\quad}{18}$	23.	$\frac{7}{9} = \frac{\quad}{72}$
12.	$\frac{2}{7} = \frac{6}{\quad}$	24.	$\frac{8}{9} = \frac{104}{\quad}$

417 A | Fill in the missing part of the fraction. | Second Half

1.	$\frac{1}{3} = \frac{}{6}$	13.	$\frac{5}{7} = \frac{}{49}$
2.	$\frac{1}{2} = \frac{}{4}$	14.	$\frac{4}{7} = \frac{16}{}$
3.	$\frac{1}{6} = \frac{}{18}$	15.	$\frac{3}{7} = \frac{}{42}$
4.	$\frac{1}{5} = \frac{}{15}$	16.	$\frac{1}{8} = \frac{}{64}$
5.	$\frac{1}{4} = \frac{}{8}$	17.	$\frac{3}{8} = \frac{15}{}$
6.	$\frac{2}{3} = \frac{6}{}$	18.	$\frac{5}{8} = \frac{}{72}$
7.	$\frac{3}{4} = \frac{9}{}$	19.	$\frac{7}{8} = \frac{56}{}$
8.	$\frac{2}{7} = \frac{6}{}$	20.	$\frac{1}{9} = \frac{5}{}$
9.	$\frac{3}{10} = \frac{}{40}$	21.	$\frac{2}{9} = \frac{}{36}$
10.	$\frac{3}{5} = \frac{15}{}$	22.	$\frac{5}{9} = \frac{}{72}$
11.	$\frac{5}{6} = \frac{}{18}$	23.	$\frac{7}{9} = \frac{}{72}$
12.	$\frac{2}{10} = \frac{6}{}$	24.	$\frac{8}{9} = \frac{120}{}$

417 B — Fill in the missing part of the fraction. — First Half

1.	$\frac{1}{2} = \frac{}{4}$	13.	$\frac{1}{} = \frac{15}{270}$
2.	$\frac{1}{3} = \frac{}{6}$	14.	$\frac{}{84} = \frac{1}{3}$
3.	$\frac{1}{4} = \frac{}{8}$	15.	$\frac{1}{4} = \frac{}{140}$
4.	$\frac{}{27} = \frac{1}{9}$	16.	$\frac{1}{8} = \frac{}{64}$
5.	$\frac{}{36} = \frac{1}{12}$	17.	$\frac{3}{8} = \frac{15}{}$
6.	$\frac{}{54} = \frac{1}{6}$	18.	$\frac{5}{8} = \frac{}{72}$
7.	$\frac{1}{6} = \frac{}{72}$	19.	$\frac{7}{8} = \frac{56}{}$
8.	$\frac{2}{6} = \frac{}{90}$	20.	$\frac{}{360} = \frac{1}{8}$
9.	$\frac{}{216} = \frac{1}{18}$	21.	$\frac{1}{25} = \frac{}{200}$
10.	$\frac{3}{5} = \frac{15}{}$	22.	$\frac{5}{9} = \frac{}{72}$
11.	$\frac{5}{6} = \frac{}{18}$	23.	$\frac{7}{9} = \frac{}{72}$
12.	$\frac{2}{7} = \frac{6}{}$	24.	$\frac{8}{9} = \frac{104}{}$

417 B | Fill in the missing part of the fraction. | Second Half

1.	$\frac{1}{3} = \frac{\quad}{6}$	13.	$\frac{1}{\quad} = \frac{15}{525}$
2.	$\frac{1}{2} = \frac{\quad}{4}$	14.	$\frac{\quad}{84} = \frac{1}{3}$
3.	$\frac{\quad}{36} = \frac{1}{12}$	15.	$\frac{1}{4} = \frac{\quad}{72}$
4.	$\frac{\quad}{27} = \frac{1}{9}$	16.	$\frac{1}{8} = \frac{\quad}{64}$
5.	$\frac{1}{4} = \frac{\quad}{8}$	17.	$\frac{3}{8} = \frac{15}{\quad}$
6.	$\frac{\quad}{54} = \frac{1}{6}$	18.	$\frac{5}{8} = \frac{\quad}{72}$
7.	$\frac{1}{6} = \frac{\quad}{72}$	19.	$\frac{7}{8} = \frac{56}{\quad}$
8.	$\frac{1}{2} = \frac{\quad}{42}$	20.	$\frac{\quad}{315} = \frac{1}{7}$
9.	$\frac{\quad}{192} = \frac{1}{16}$	21.	$\frac{1}{25} = \frac{\quad}{200}$
10.	$\frac{3}{5} = \frac{15}{\quad}$	22.	$\frac{5}{9} = \frac{\quad}{72}$
11.	$\frac{5}{6} = \frac{\quad}{18}$	23.	$\frac{7}{9} = \frac{\quad}{72}$
12.	$\frac{2}{3} = \frac{\quad}{45}$	24.	$\frac{1}{4} = \frac{\quad}{540}$

418 A Add. All answers must be in simplest form. First Half

1.	$\frac{1}{3} + \frac{1}{3} =$	11.	$\frac{2}{5} + \frac{1}{10} =$
2.	$\frac{1}{5} + \frac{1}{5} =$	12.	$\frac{3}{8} + \frac{1}{4} =$
3.	$\frac{1}{6} + \frac{1}{6} =$	13.	$\frac{3}{8} + \frac{1}{2} =$
4.	$\frac{1}{4} + \frac{1}{2} =$	14.	$\frac{5}{6} + \frac{1}{6} =$
5.	$\frac{1}{4} + \frac{1}{4} =$	15.	$\frac{1}{7} + \frac{3}{7} =$
6.	$\frac{1}{2} + \frac{1}{2} =$	16.	$\frac{1}{7} + \frac{5}{14} =$
7.	$\frac{1}{8} + \frac{3}{8} =$	17.	$\frac{1}{8} + \frac{1}{16} =$
8.	$\frac{1}{10} + \frac{1}{10} =$	18.	$\frac{2}{3} + \frac{1}{9} =$
9.	$\frac{1}{10} + \frac{1}{5} =$	19.	$\frac{5}{12} + \frac{5}{12} =$
10.	$\frac{1}{10} + \frac{7}{10} =$	20.	$\frac{1}{3} + \frac{2}{3} =$

418 A Add. All answers must be in simplest form. Second Half

1.	$\frac{1}{5} + \frac{1}{5} =$	11.	$\frac{3}{8} + \frac{1}{4} =$
2.	$\frac{1}{3} + \frac{1}{3} =$	12.	$\frac{2}{5} + \frac{1}{10} =$
3.	$\frac{1}{6} + \frac{1}{6} =$	13.	$\frac{3}{8} + \frac{1}{2} =$
4.	$\frac{1}{4} + \frac{1}{2} =$	14.	$\frac{5}{6} + \frac{1}{6} =$
5.	$\frac{1}{2} + \frac{1}{2} =$	15.	$\frac{1}{7} + \frac{3}{7} =$
6.	$\frac{1}{4} + \frac{1}{4} =$	16.	$\frac{1}{7} + \frac{5}{14} =$
7.	$\frac{1}{8} + \frac{3}{8} =$	17.	$\frac{1}{8} + \frac{1}{16} =$
8.	$\frac{1}{10} + \frac{1}{10} =$	18.	$\frac{2}{3} + \frac{1}{9} =$
9.	$\frac{1}{10} + \frac{1}{5} =$	19.	$\frac{5}{12} + \frac{5}{12} =$
10.	$\frac{1}{10} + \frac{7}{10} =$	20.	$\frac{1}{3} + \frac{2}{3} =$

418 B Add. All answers must be in simplest form. First Half

1.	$\frac{1}{3} + \frac{1}{3} =$	11.	$\frac{1}{5} + \frac{1}{10} + \frac{1}{5} =$
2.	$\frac{1}{5} + \frac{1}{5} =$	12.	$\frac{1}{8} + \frac{1}{4} + \frac{1}{4} =$
3.	$\frac{1}{6} + \frac{1}{12} + \frac{1}{12} =$	13.	$\frac{3}{8} + \frac{1}{2} =$
4.	$\frac{1}{4} + \frac{1}{2} =$	14.	$\frac{1}{3} + \frac{1}{6} + \frac{1}{2} =$
5.	$\frac{1}{8} + \frac{1}{4} + \frac{1}{8} =$	15.	$\frac{1}{7} + \frac{3}{7} =$
6.	$\frac{1}{8} + \frac{1}{4} + \frac{5}{8} =$	16.	$\frac{1}{7} + \frac{5}{14} =$
7.	$\frac{1}{9} + \frac{5}{18} + \frac{1}{9} =$	17.	$\frac{1}{32} + \frac{1}{8} + \frac{1}{32} =$
8.	$\frac{1}{20} + \frac{1}{20} + \frac{1}{10} =$	18.	$\frac{1}{3} + \frac{1}{9} + \frac{1}{3} =$
9.	$\frac{1}{10} + \frac{1}{5} =$	19.	$\frac{1}{12} + \frac{7}{12} + \frac{1}{6} =$
10.	$\frac{1}{10} + \frac{7}{10} =$	20.	$\frac{1}{3} + \frac{2}{3} =$

418 B Add. All answers must be in simplest form. Second Half

1.	$\frac{1}{5}+\frac{1}{5}=$	11.	$\frac{1}{8}+\frac{1}{4}+\frac{1}{4}=$
2.	$\frac{1}{3}+\frac{1}{3}=$	12.	$\frac{1}{5}+\frac{1}{10}+\frac{1}{5}=$
3.	$\frac{1}{6}+\frac{1}{12}+\frac{1}{12}=$	13.	$\frac{3}{8}+\frac{1}{2}=$
4.	$\frac{1}{4}+\frac{1}{2}=$	14.	$\frac{1}{3}+\frac{1}{6}+\frac{1}{2}=$
5.	$\frac{1}{8}+\frac{1}{4}+\frac{5}{8}=$	15.	$\frac{1}{7}+\frac{3}{7}=$
6.	$\frac{1}{8}+\frac{1}{4}+\frac{1}{8}=$	16.	$\frac{1}{7}+\frac{5}{14}=$
7.	$\frac{1}{9}+\frac{5}{18}+\frac{1}{9}=$	17.	$\frac{1}{32}+\frac{1}{8}+\frac{1}{32}=$
8.	$\frac{1}{20}+\frac{1}{20}+\frac{1}{10}=$	18.	$\frac{1}{3}+\frac{1}{9}+\frac{1}{3}=$
9.	$\frac{1}{10}+\frac{1}{5}=$	19.	$\frac{1}{12}+\frac{7}{12}+\frac{1}{6}=$
10.	$\frac{1}{10}+\frac{7}{10}=$	20.	$\frac{1}{3}+\frac{2}{3}=$

419 A Give the answer in simplest form. First Half

1.	$\frac{1}{3}+\frac{1}{3}=$	16.	$1-\frac{1}{8}-\frac{2}{8}=$
2.	$\frac{1}{5}+\frac{1}{5}=$	17.	$\frac{3}{4}-\frac{1}{4}=$
3.	$\frac{2}{5}+\frac{2}{5}=$	18.	$\frac{5}{6}-\frac{1}{6}=$
4.	$\frac{1}{7}+\frac{3}{7}=$	19.	$\frac{5}{6}-\frac{1}{3}=$
5.	$\frac{2}{7}+\frac{4}{7}=$	20.	$\frac{3}{4}-\frac{3}{8}=$
6.	$\frac{1}{8}+\frac{1}{8}=$	21.	$\frac{9}{10}-\frac{1}{5}=$
7.	$\frac{1}{8}+\frac{2}{8}=$	22.	$\frac{1}{4}+\frac{2}{2}+\frac{1}{4}=$
8.	$\frac{3}{8}+\frac{2}{8}=$	23.	$\frac{1}{5}+\frac{2}{5}+\frac{1}{5}=$
9.	$\frac{1}{9}+\frac{2}{9}=$	24.	$\frac{1}{5}+\frac{1}{10}+\frac{3}{10}=$
10.	$\frac{4}{9}+\frac{1}{9}=$	25.	$\frac{7}{10}-\frac{3}{5}=$
11.	$1-\frac{1}{3}=$	26.	$\frac{9}{10}-\frac{1}{2}=$
12.	$1-\frac{2}{3}=$	27.	$\frac{3}{4}-\frac{7}{12}=$
13.	$1-\frac{1}{4}=$	28.	$\frac{7}{8}-\frac{1}{4}=$
14.	$1-\frac{1}{3}-\frac{1}{3}=$	29.	$\frac{11}{12}-\frac{2}{3}=$
15.	$1-\frac{1}{9}-\frac{2}{9}=$	30.	$\frac{7}{12}-\frac{1}{3}-\frac{1}{4}=$

419 A — Give the answer in simplest form. — Second Half

1.	$\frac{1}{5}+\frac{1}{5}=$	16.	$1-\frac{1}{8}-\frac{1}{8}=$
2.	$\frac{1}{3}+\frac{1}{3}=$	17.	$\frac{5}{6}-\frac{1}{6}=$
3.	$\frac{1}{7}+\frac{3}{7}=$	18.	$\frac{3}{4}-\frac{1}{4}=$
4.	$\frac{2}{5}+\frac{2}{5}=$	19.	$\frac{5}{6}-\frac{1}{3}=$
5.	$\frac{2}{7}+\frac{4}{7}=$	20.	$\frac{3}{4}-\frac{3}{8}=$
6.	$\frac{1}{6}+\frac{1}{6}=$	21.	$\frac{9}{10}-\frac{1}{5}=$
7.	$\frac{1}{8}+\frac{2}{8}=$	22.	$\frac{1}{4}+\frac{2}{2}+\frac{1}{4}=$
8.	$\frac{3}{8}+\frac{2}{8}=$	23.	$\frac{1}{5}+\frac{2}{5}+\frac{1}{5}=$
9.	$\frac{1}{9}+\frac{2}{9}=$	24.	$\frac{1}{5}+\frac{1}{10}+\frac{3}{10}=$
10.	$\frac{4}{9}+\frac{1}{9}=$	25.	$\frac{7}{10}-\frac{3}{5}=$
11.	$1-\frac{1}{3}=$	26.	$\frac{9}{10}-\frac{1}{2}=$
12.	$1-\frac{2}{3}=$	27.	$\frac{3}{4}-\frac{7}{12}=$
13.	$1-\frac{1}{4}=$	28.	$\frac{7}{8}-\frac{1}{4}=$
14.	$1-\frac{1}{3}-\frac{1}{3}=$	29.	$\frac{11}{12}-\frac{2}{3}=$
15.	$1-\frac{1}{9}-\frac{2}{9}=$	30.	$\frac{7}{12}-\frac{1}{3}-\frac{1}{4}=$

419 B Give the answer in simplest form. First Half

1.	$1-\frac{1}{3}=$	16.	$1-\frac{1}{8}-\frac{2}{8}=$
2.	$1-\frac{3}{5}=$	17.	$\frac{3}{32}+\frac{1}{4}+\frac{1}{8}+\frac{1}{32}=$
3.	$\frac{1}{5}+\frac{1}{5}+\frac{2}{5}=$	18.	$\frac{5}{6}-\frac{1}{6}=$
4.	$1-\frac{3}{7}=$	19.	$\frac{5}{6}-\frac{1}{3}=$
5.	$\frac{1}{7}+\frac{2}{7}+\frac{3}{7}=$	20.	$1-\frac{1}{4}-\frac{3}{8}=$
6.	$1-\frac{1}{2}-\frac{1}{4}=$	21.	$\frac{1}{3}+\frac{8}{30}+\frac{1}{10}=$
7.	$1-\frac{1}{4}-\frac{3}{8}=$	22.	$\frac{3}{8}+\frac{1}{2}+\frac{1}{8}=$
8.	$\frac{1}{8}+\frac{1}{4}+\frac{1}{4}=$	23.	$1-\frac{1}{5}=$
9.	$1-\frac{2}{9}-\frac{4}{9}=$	24.	$\frac{1}{5}+\frac{1}{10}+\frac{3}{10}=$
10.	$\frac{1}{6}+\frac{1}{3}+\frac{1}{18}=$	25.	$\frac{7}{10}-\frac{3}{5}=$
11.	$\frac{1}{6}+\frac{1}{6}+\frac{1}{3}=$	26.	$\frac{9}{40}+\frac{7}{40}=$
12.	$1-\frac{2}{3}=$	27.	$\frac{3}{4}-\frac{7}{12}=$
13.	$1-\frac{1}{4}=$	28.	$\frac{1}{16}+\frac{3}{16}+\frac{3}{8}=$
14.	$1-\frac{1}{3}-\frac{1}{3}=$	29.	$\frac{11}{12}-\frac{2}{3}=$
15.	$\frac{2}{9}+\frac{1}{3}+\frac{1}{9}=$	30.	$\frac{7}{12}-\frac{1}{3}-\frac{1}{4}=$

419 B — Give the answer in simplest form. — Second Half

1.	$1-\frac{3}{5}=$	16.	$1-\frac{1}{8}-\frac{1}{8}=$
2.	$1-\frac{1}{3}=$	17.	$\frac{5}{6}-\frac{1}{6}=$
3.	$1-\frac{3}{7}=$	18.	$\frac{3}{32}+\frac{1}{4}+\frac{1}{8}+\frac{1}{32}=$
4.	$\frac{1}{5}+\frac{1}{5}+\frac{2}{5}=$	19.	$\frac{5}{6}-\frac{1}{3}=$
5.	$\frac{1}{7}+\frac{2}{7}+\frac{3}{7}=$	20.	$1-\frac{1}{4}-\frac{3}{8}=$
6.	$1-\frac{1}{2}-\frac{1}{6}=$	21.	$\frac{1}{3}+\frac{8}{30}+\frac{1}{10}=$
7.	$1-\frac{1}{4}-\frac{3}{8}=$	22.	$\frac{3}{8}+\frac{1}{2}+\frac{1}{8}=$
8.	$\frac{1}{8}+\frac{1}{4}+\frac{1}{4}=$	23.	$1-\frac{1}{5}=$
9.	$1-\frac{2}{9}-\frac{4}{9}=$	24.	$\frac{1}{5}+\frac{1}{10}+\frac{3}{10}=$
10.	$\frac{1}{6}+\frac{1}{3}+\frac{1}{18}=$	25.	$\frac{7}{10}-\frac{3}{5}=$
11.	$\frac{1}{6}+\frac{1}{6}+\frac{1}{3}=$	26.	$\frac{9}{40}+\frac{7}{40}=$
12.	$1-\frac{2}{3}=$	27.	$\frac{3}{4}-\frac{7}{12}=$
13.	$1-\frac{1}{4}=$	28.	$\frac{1}{16}+\frac{3}{16}+\frac{3}{8}=$
14.	$1-\frac{1}{3}-\frac{1}{3}=$	29.	$\frac{11}{12}-\frac{2}{3}=$
15.	$\frac{2}{9}+\frac{1}{3}+\frac{1}{9}=$	30.	$\frac{7}{12}-\frac{1}{3}-\frac{1}{4}=$

420 A | Change to a whole or mixed number. | First Half

1.	$\frac{4}{3}$ =	16.	$\frac{8}{7}$ =
2.	$\frac{6}{5}$ =	17.	$\frac{14}{7}$ =
3.	$\frac{10}{9}$ =	18.	$\frac{13}{7}$ =
4.	$\frac{8}{7}$ =	19.	$\frac{10}{7}$ =
5.	$\frac{8}{5}$ =	20.	$\frac{12}{7}$ =
6.	$\frac{9}{5}$ =	21.	$\frac{16}{5}$ =
7.	$\frac{5}{4}$ =	22.	$\frac{19}{5}$ =
8.	$\frac{8}{3}$ =	23.	$\frac{18}{9}$ =
9.	$\frac{11}{3}$ =	24.	$\frac{36}{27}$ =
10.	$\frac{7}{6}$ =	25.	$\frac{13}{9}$ =
11.	$\frac{9}{5}$ =	26.	$\frac{16}{9}$ =
12.	$\frac{8}{5}$ =	27.	$\frac{20}{9}$ =
13.	$\frac{11}{5}$ =	28.	$\frac{23}{10}$ =
14.	$\frac{12}{5}$ =	29.	$\frac{29}{10}$ =
15.	$\frac{14}{5}$ =	30.	$\frac{31}{10}$ =

420 A Change to a whole or mixed number. Second Half

1.	$\frac{3}{2}$ =	16.	$\frac{13}{12}$ =
2.	$\frac{7}{6}$ =	17.	$\frac{14}{7}$ =
3.	$\frac{9}{8}$ =	18.	$\frac{13}{7}$ =
4.	$\frac{8}{7}$ =	19.	$\frac{10}{7}$ =
5.	$\frac{7}{5}$ =	20.	$\frac{12}{7}$ =
6.	$\frac{9}{5}$ =	21.	$\frac{16}{5}$ =
7.	$\frac{5}{4}$ =	22.	$\frac{19}{5}$ =
8.	$\frac{8}{3}$ =	23.	$\frac{18}{9}$ =
9.	$\frac{10}{3}$ =	24.	$\frac{36}{27}$ =
10.	$\frac{11}{6}$ =	25.	$\frac{13}{9}$ =
11.	$\frac{9}{5}$ =	26.	$\frac{16}{9}$ =
12.	$\frac{8}{5}$ =	27.	$\frac{20}{9}$ =
13.	$\frac{11}{5}$ =	28.	$\frac{23}{10}$ =
14.	$\frac{12}{5}$ =	29.	$\frac{29}{10}$ =
15.	$\frac{14}{5}$ =	30.	$\frac{31}{10}$ =

420 B Change to a whole or mixed number. First Half

1.	$\frac{4}{3}$ =	16.	$\frac{16}{14}$ =
2.	$\frac{6}{5}$ =	17.	$\frac{28}{14}$ =
3.	$\frac{10}{9}$ =	18.	$\frac{13}{7}$ =
4.	$\frac{16}{14}$ =	19.	$\frac{10}{7}$ =
5.	$\frac{16}{10}$ =	20.	$\frac{24}{14}$ =
6.	$\frac{18}{10}$ =	21.	$\frac{32}{10}$ =
7.	$\frac{10}{8}$ =	22.	$\frac{19}{5}$ =
8.	$\frac{16}{6}$ =	23.	$\frac{18}{9}$ =
9.	$\frac{22}{6}$ =	24.	$\frac{12}{9}$ =
10.	$\frac{7}{6}$ =	25.	$\frac{26}{18}$ =
11.	$\frac{9}{5}$ =	26.	$\frac{16}{9}$ =
12.	$\frac{24}{15}$ =	27.	$\frac{40}{18}$ =
13.	$\frac{22}{10}$ =	28.	$\frac{46}{20}$ =
14.	$\frac{36}{15}$ =	29.	$\frac{29}{10}$ =
15.	$\frac{14}{5}$ =	30.	$\frac{62}{20}$ =

420 B Change to a whole or mixed number. Second Half

1.	$\frac{3}{2}$ =	16.	$\frac{26}{24}$ =
2.	$\frac{7}{6}$ =	17.	$\frac{28}{14}$ =
3.	$\frac{9}{8}$ =	18.	$\frac{13}{7}$ =
4.	$\frac{16}{14}$ =	19.	$\frac{10}{7}$ =
5.	$\frac{14}{10}$ =	20.	$\frac{24}{14}$ =
6.	$\frac{18}{10}$ =	21.	$\frac{32}{10}$ =
7.	$\frac{10}{8}$ =	22.	$\frac{19}{5}$ =
8.	$\frac{16}{6}$ =	23.	$\frac{18}{9}$ =
9.	$\frac{30}{9}$ =	24.	$\frac{12}{9}$ =
10.	$\frac{22}{12}$ =	25.	$\frac{26}{18}$ =
11.	$\frac{9}{5}$ =	26.	$\frac{16}{9}$ =
12.	$\frac{24}{15}$ =	27.	$\frac{40}{18}$ =
13.	$\frac{22}{10}$ =	28.	$\frac{46}{20}$ =
14.	$\frac{36}{15}$ =	29.	$\frac{29}{10}$ =
15.	$\frac{14}{5}$ =	30.	$\frac{62}{20}$ =

421 A | Simplify. | First Half

1.	$\frac{4}{2}$ =	11.	$2\frac{4}{8}$ =
2.	$\frac{8}{4}$ =	12.	$4\frac{3}{6}$ =
3.	$\frac{7}{4}$ =	13.	$4\frac{6}{8}$ =
4.	$\frac{12}{5}$ =	14.	$7\frac{4}{8}$ =
5.	$\frac{10}{5}$ =	15.	$1\frac{8}{5}$ =
6.	$\frac{12}{6}$ =	16.	$2\frac{10}{9}$ =
7.	$\frac{20}{5}$ =	17.	$3\frac{7}{6}$ =
8.	$\frac{18}{5}$ =	18.	$5\frac{12}{10}$ =
9.	$\frac{17}{8}$ =	19.	$2\frac{10}{5}$ =
10.	$\frac{20}{8}$ =	20.	$5\frac{18}{6}$ =

421 A Simplify. Second Half

1.	$\frac{6}{3} =$	11.	$2\frac{4}{8} =$
2.	$\frac{10}{5} =$	12.	$4\frac{3}{6} =$
3.	$\frac{5}{3} =$	13.	$4\frac{6}{8} =$
4.	$\frac{15}{5} =$	14.	$7\frac{4}{8} =$
5.	$\frac{10}{5} =$	15.	$1\frac{8}{5} =$
6.	$\frac{12}{6} =$	16.	$2\frac{10}{9} =$
7.	$\frac{20}{5} =$	17.	$3\frac{7}{6} =$
8.	$\frac{18}{5} =$	18.	$5\frac{12}{10} =$
9.	$\frac{17}{8} =$	19.	$2\frac{10}{5} =$
10.	$\frac{20}{8} =$	20.	$5\frac{18}{6} =$

421 B | Simplify. | First Half

1.	$\frac{4}{2} =$	11.	$2\frac{76}{152} =$
2.	$\frac{8}{4} =$	12.	$4\frac{19}{38} =$
3.	$\frac{7}{4} =$	13.	$4\frac{42}{56} =$
4.	$\frac{120}{50} =$	14.	$7\frac{49}{98} =$
5.	$\frac{200}{100} =$	15.	$1\frac{8}{5} =$
6.	$\frac{240}{120} =$	16.	$2\frac{10}{9} =$
7.	$\frac{140}{35} =$	17.	$3\frac{7}{6} =$
8.	$\frac{108}{30} =$	18.	$5\frac{12}{10} =$
9.	$\frac{51}{24} =$	19.	$\frac{720}{180} =$
10.	$\frac{140}{56} =$	20.	$\frac{336}{42} =$

421 B Simplify. Second Half

1.	$\frac{6}{3} =$	11.	$2\frac{87}{174} =$
2.	$\frac{10}{5} =$	12.	$4\frac{64}{128} =$
3.	$\frac{5}{3} =$	13.	$4\frac{42}{56} =$
4.	$\frac{130}{50} =$	14.	$7\frac{49}{98} =$
5.	$\frac{150}{50} =$	15.	$1\frac{8}{5} =$
6.	$\frac{140}{70} =$	16.	$2\frac{10}{9} =$
7.	$\frac{140}{35} =$	17.	$3\frac{7}{6} =$
8.	$\frac{108}{30} =$	18.	$5\frac{12}{10} =$
9.	$\frac{51}{24} =$	19.	$\frac{640}{160} =$
10.	$\frac{140}{56} =$	20.	$\frac{360}{45} =$

422 A — Change to an improper fraction. — First Half

1.	$1\frac{1}{2}$ =	16.	$3\frac{2}{3}$ =
2.	$1\frac{1}{4}$ =	17.	$3\frac{3}{8}$ =
3.	$1\frac{1}{6}$ =	18.	$3\frac{7}{8}$ =
4.	$1\frac{3}{4}$ =	19.	$4\frac{1}{4}$ =
5.	$1\frac{5}{6}$ =	20.	$4\frac{2}{3}$ =
6.	$1\frac{7}{8}$ =	21.	$4\frac{3}{5}$ =
7.	$2\frac{1}{4}$ =	22.	$4\frac{2}{5}$ =
8.	$2\frac{1}{3}$ =	23.	$4\frac{1}{6}$ =
9.	$2\frac{2}{3}$ =	24.	$4\frac{2}{7}$ =
10.	$2\frac{3}{4}$ =	25.	$4\frac{1}{8}$ =
11.	$2\frac{2}{5}$ =	26.	$4\frac{3}{10}$ =
12.	$2\frac{4}{7}$ =	27.	$5\frac{1}{9}$ =
13.	$2\frac{5}{6}$ =	28.	$5\frac{4}{9}$ =
14.	$3\frac{1}{2}$ =	29.	$5\frac{5}{9}$ =
15.	$3\frac{1}{5}$ =	30.	$5\frac{7}{9}$ =

422 A Change to an improper fraction. Second Half

1.	$1\frac{1}{3}$ =	16.	$3\frac{2}{5}$ =
2.	$1\frac{1}{2}$ =	17.	$3\frac{5}{7}$ =
3.	$1\frac{1}{5}$ =	18.	$3\frac{7}{8}$ =
4.	$1\frac{2}{3}$ =	19.	$4\frac{1}{4}$ =
5.	$1\frac{4}{7}$ =	20.	$4\frac{2}{3}$ =
6.	$1\frac{7}{8}$ =	21.	$4\frac{3}{4}$ =
7.	$2\frac{1}{4}$ =	22.	$4\frac{2}{5}$ =
8.	$2\frac{1}{3}$ =	23.	$4\frac{1}{6}$ =
9.	$2\frac{2}{3}$ =	24.	$4\frac{2}{7}$ =
10.	$2\frac{3}{4}$ =	25.	$4\frac{1}{8}$ =
11.	$2\frac{2}{5}$ =	26.	$4\frac{3}{10}$ =
12.	$2\frac{4}{7}$ =	27.	$5\frac{1}{9}$ =
13.	$2\frac{5}{6}$ =	28.	$5\frac{4}{9}$ =
14.	$3\frac{1}{2}$ =	29.	$5\frac{5}{9}$ =
15.	$3\frac{1}{5}$ =	30.	$5\frac{7}{9}$ =

422 B Change to an improper fraction and simplify. First Half

1.	$1\frac{1}{2}$ =	16.	$3\frac{4}{6}$ =
2.	$1\frac{1}{4}$ =	17.	$3\frac{12}{32}$ =
3.	$1\frac{1}{6}$ =	18.	$3\frac{21}{24}$ =
4.	$1\frac{3}{4}$ =	19.	$4\frac{1}{4}$ =
5.	$1\frac{10}{12}$ =	20.	$4\frac{2}{3}$ =
6.	$1\frac{14}{16}$ =	21.	$4\frac{3}{5}$ =
7.	$2\frac{3}{12}$ =	22.	$4\frac{2}{5}$ =
8.	$2\frac{3}{9}$ =	23.	$4\frac{3}{18}$ =
9.	$2\frac{6}{9}$ =	24.	$4\frac{6}{21}$ =
10.	$2\frac{12}{16}$ =	25.	$4\frac{3}{24}$ =
11.	$2\frac{4}{10}$ =	26.	$4\frac{9}{30}$ =
12.	$2\frac{8}{14}$ =	27.	$5\frac{2}{18}$ =
13.	$2\frac{10}{12}$ =	28.	$5\frac{8}{18}$ =
14.	$3\frac{15}{30}$ =	29.	$5\frac{10}{18}$ =
15.	$3\frac{5}{25}$ =	30.	$5\frac{14}{18}$ =

422 B | Change to an improper fraction and simplify. | Second Half

1.	$1\frac{1}{3}$ =	16.	$3\frac{2}{5}$ =
2.	$1\frac{1}{2}$ =	17.	$3\frac{5}{7}$ =
3.	$1\frac{1}{5}$ =	18.	$3\frac{21}{24}$ =
4.	$1\frac{2}{3}$ =	19.	$4\frac{1}{4}$ =
5.	$1\frac{4}{7}$ =	20.	$4\frac{2}{3}$ =
6.	$1\frac{14}{16}$ =	21.	$4\frac{3}{4}$ =
7.	$2\frac{3}{12}$ =	22.	$4\frac{2}{5}$ =
8.	$2\frac{3}{9}$ =	23.	$4\frac{3}{18}$ =
9.	$2\frac{6}{9}$ =	24.	$4\frac{6}{21}$ =
10.	$2\frac{12}{16}$ =	25.	$4\frac{3}{24}$ =
11.	$2\frac{4}{10}$ =	26.	$4\frac{9}{30}$ =
12.	$2\frac{8}{14}$ =	27.	$5\frac{2}{18}$ =
13.	$2\frac{10}{12}$ =	28.	$5\frac{8}{18}$ =
14.	$3\frac{15}{30}$ =	29.	$5\frac{10}{18}$ =
15.	$3\frac{5}{25}$ =	30.	$5\frac{14}{18}$ =

423 A | Find the value. | First Half

1.	$\frac{1}{2}$ of 10 =	13.	$\frac{1}{10}$ of 100 =
2.	$\frac{1}{2}$ of 18 =	14.	$\frac{1}{5}$ of 100 =
3.	$\frac{1}{3}$ of 6 =	15.	$\frac{2}{5}$ of 100 =
4.	$\frac{2}{3}$ of 6 =	16.	$\frac{4}{5}$ of 100 =
5.	$\frac{1}{4}$ of 8 =	17.	$\frac{1}{4}$ of 100 =
6.	$\frac{3}{4}$ of 8 =	18.	$\frac{3}{4}$ of 100 =
7.	$\frac{2}{3}$ of 9 =	19.	$\frac{1}{3}$ of 30 =
8.	$\frac{2}{3}$ of 18 =	20.	$\frac{2}{3}$ of 30 =
9.	$\frac{1}{8}$ of 24 =	21.	$\frac{3}{10}$ of 30 =
10.	$\frac{3}{8}$ of 24 =	22.	$\frac{9}{10}$ of 30 =
11.	$\frac{5}{8}$ of 24 =	23.	$\frac{1}{3}$ of 2 =
12.	$\frac{7}{8}$ of 24 =	24.	$\frac{1}{5}$ of 3 =

423 A Find the value. Second Half

1.	$\frac{1}{2}$ of 6 =	13.	$\frac{1}{10}$ of 50 =
2.	$\frac{1}{2}$ of 12 =	14.	$\frac{1}{5}$ of 50 =
3.	$\frac{1}{3}$ of 9 =	15.	$\frac{2}{5}$ of 50 =
4.	$\frac{2}{3}$ of 9 =	16.	$\frac{4}{5}$ of 50 =
5.	$\frac{1}{4}$ of 12 =	17.	$\frac{1}{4}$ of 100 =
6.	$\frac{3}{4}$ of 12 =	18.	$\frac{3}{4}$ of 100 =
7.	$\frac{1}{3}$ of 9 =	19.	$\frac{1}{3}$ of 30 =
8.	$\frac{1}{3}$ of 18 =	20.	$\frac{2}{3}$ of 30 =
9.	$\frac{1}{8}$ of 24 =	21.	$\frac{3}{10}$ of 30 =
10.	$\frac{3}{8}$ of 24 =	22.	$\frac{9}{10}$ of 30 =
11.	$\frac{5}{8}$ of 24 =	23.	$\frac{1}{8}$ of 3 =
12.	$\frac{7}{8}$ of 24 =	24.	$\frac{1}{5}$ of 4 =

423 B — Find the value. — First Half

1.	$\frac{1}{8}$ of 40 =	13.	$\frac{5}{9}$ of 18 =
2.	$\frac{1}{6}$ of 54 =	14.	$\frac{2}{9}$ of 90 =
3.	$\frac{1}{9}$ of 18 =	15.	$\frac{2}{9}$ of 180 =
4.	$\frac{1}{12}$ of 48 =	16.	$\frac{4}{5}$ of 100 =
5.	$\frac{2}{9}$ of 9 =	17.	$\frac{1}{15}$ of 375 =
6.	$\frac{1}{9}$ of 54 =	18.	$\frac{1}{8}$ of 600 =
7.	$\frac{2}{3}$ of 9 =	19.	$\frac{1}{4}$ of 40 =
8.	$\frac{3}{7}$ of 28 =	20.	$\frac{4}{10}$ of 50 =
9.	$\frac{1}{12}$ of 36 =	21.	$\frac{3}{10}$ of 30 =
10.	$\frac{1}{7}$ of 63 =	22.	$\frac{1}{3}$ of 81 =
11.	$\frac{3}{9}$ of 45 =	23.	$\frac{1}{3}$ of 2 =
12.	$\frac{7}{8}$ of 24 =	24.	$\frac{1}{5}$ of 3 =

423 B | Find the value. | Second Half

1.	$\frac{1}{8}$ of 24 =	13.	$\frac{3}{30}$ of 50 =
2.	$\frac{1}{9}$ of 54 =	14.	$\frac{3}{15}$ of 50 =
3.	$\frac{1}{9}$ of 27 =	15.	$\frac{8}{20}$ of 50 =
4.	$\frac{1}{12}$ of 72 =	16.	$\frac{20}{25}$ of 50 =
5.	$\frac{3}{9}$ of 9 =	17.	$\frac{1}{15}$ of 375 =
6.	$\frac{1}{6}$ of 54 =	18.	$\frac{1}{8}$ of 600 =
7.	$\frac{1}{11}$ of 33 =	19.	$\frac{1}{4}$ of 40 =
8.	$\frac{1}{7}$ of 42 =	20.	$\frac{4}{10}$ of 50 =
9.	$\frac{1}{12}$ of 36 =	21.	$\frac{3}{10}$ of 30 =
10.	$\frac{1}{7}$ of 63 =	22.	$\frac{1}{3}$ of 81 =
11.	$\frac{3}{9}$ of 45 =	23.	$\frac{1}{8}$ of 3 =
12.	$\frac{7}{8}$ of 24 =	24.	$\frac{1}{5}$ of 4 =

424 A | Add. | First Half

1.	2 + 2 =	16.	2.7 + 1.3 =
2.	0.2 + 0.2 =	17.	2.8 + 1.4 =
3.	0.02 + 0.02 =	18.	3.6 + 5 =
4.	2 + 0.2 =	19.	3.6 + 5.5 =
5.	0.2 + 0.02 =	20.	3.8 + 6.7 =
6.	2 + 0.02 =	21.	0.63 + 0.7 =
7.	0.4 + 0.5 =	22.	0.48 + 0.09 =
8.	0.9 + 0.4 =	23.	0.36 + 0.24 =
9.	0.8 + 0.5 =	24.	2.36 + 0.24 =
10.	0.09 + 0.04 =	25.	21.2 + 2.39 =
11.	0.4 + 0.8 =	26.	21.2 + 3.98 =
12.	2.2 + 0.3 =	27.	26.48 + 4.79 =
13.	2.2 + 0.7 =	28.	29.03 + 3.7 =
14.	2.2 + 0.8 =	29.	29.98 + 2.09 =
15.	2.6 + 1.3 =	30.	30.99 + 9.99 =

424 A | Add. | Second Half

1.	1 + 1 =	16.	2.7 + 1.3 =
2.	0.1 + 0.1 =	17.	2.7 + 1.5 =
3.	0.01 + 0.01 =	18.	3.6 + 5 =
4.	1 + 0.1 =	19.	3.6 + 5.5 =
5.	0.1 + 0.01 =	20.	3.8 + 6.7 =
6.	1 + 0.01 =	21.	0.63 + 0.7 =
7.	0.2 + 0.3 =	22.	0.48 + 0.09 =
8.	0.8 + 0.3 =	23.	0.36 + 0.24 =
9.	0.7 + 0.5 =	24.	2.36 + 0.24 =
10.	0.06 + 0.03 =	25.	21.2 + 2.39 =
11.	0.5 + 0.7 =	26.	21.2 + 3.98 =
12.	1.2 + 0.3 =	27.	26.48 + 4.79 =
13.	1.2 + 0.6 =	28.	19.03 + 3.4 =
14.	1.2 + 0.8 =	29.	19.98 + 2.1 =
15.	1.6 + 1.3 =	30.	20.99 + 9.99 =

424 B Add or subtract. First Half

1.	$10 - 6 =$	16.	$2.7 + 1.3 =$
2.	$1 - 0.6 =$	17.	$6.1 - 1.9 =$
3.	$1 - 0.96 =$	18.	$3.6 + 5 =$
4.	$1.5 + 0.7 =$	19.	$3.6 + 5.5 =$
5.	$0.05 + 0.17 =$	20.	$12.03 - 1.53 =$
6.	$3 - 0.98 =$	21.	$0.63 + 0.7 =$
7.	$2.1 - 1.2 =$	22.	$1.1 - 0.53 =$
8.	$0.8 + 0.3 + 0.2 =$	23.	$0.36 + 0.24 =$
9.	$2.1 - 0.8 =$	24.	$2.36 + 0.24 =$
10.	$1 - 0.87 =$	25.	$21.2 + 2.39 =$
11.	$0.35 + 0.85 =$	26.	$30 - 4.82 =$
12.	$4.1 - 1.6 =$	27.	$33.09 - 1.82 =$
13.	$5.3 - 2.4 =$	28.	$29.03 + 3.7 =$
14.	$2.2 + 0.8 =$	29.	$39.01 - 6.94 =$
15.	$6.1 - 2.2 =$	30.	$30.99 + 9.99 =$

424 B | Add or subtract. | Second Half

1.	10 – 8 =	16.	2.7 + 1.3 =
2.	1 – 0.8 =	17.	6.1 – 1.9 =
3.	1 – 0.98 =	18.	4.6 + 4 =
4.	0.5 + 0.6 =	19.	2.6 + 6.5 =
5.	0.05 + 0.06 =	20.	12.4 – 1.9 =
6.	3 – 1.99 =	21.	0.63 + 0.7 =
7.	2.1 – 1.6 =	22.	1.1 – 0.53 =
8.	0.6 + 0.3 + 0.2 =	23.	0.36 + 0.24 =
9.	2.1 – 0.9 =	24.	2.36 + 0.24 =
10.	1 – 0.91 =	25.	21.2 + 2.39 =
11.	0.35 + 0.85 =	26.	40.28 – 15.1 =
12.	4.1 – 2.6 =	27.	33.09 – 1.82 =
13.	5.3 – 3.5 =	28.	19.03 + 3.4 =
14.	0.2 + 0.8 + 1 =	29.	29. 1 – 7.02 =
15.	5.1 – 2.2 =	30.	20.99 + 9.99 =

425 A — Add or subtract. — First Half

1.	0.6 + 0.4 =	13.	3.75 + 2.2 =
2.	0.7 + 0.3 =	14.	3.75 + 2.25 =
3.	0.8 + 0.3 =	15.	3.95 + 2.05 =
4.	0.8 + 0.32 =	16.	6.1 – 2.1 =
5.	1 – 0.6 =	17.	6 – 2.1 =
6.	1 – 0.3 =	18.	6.5 – 2.4 =
7.	2 – 1.98 =	19.	6.55 – 2.4 =
8.	2 – 0.98 =	20.	7 + 3.06 =
9.	2 + 1.98 =	21.	7.2 + 3.46 =
10.	2.03 + 1.7 =	22.	7.25 + 3.45 =
11.	2.03 + 1.07 =	23.	7 – 3.9 =
12.	3.3 + 2.09 =	24.	7.2 – 3.9 =

425 A — Add or subtract. — Second Half

1.	$0.7 + 0.3 =$	13.	$3.75 + 2.1 =$
2.	$0.6 + 0.4 =$	14.	$3.75 + 2.15 =$
3.	$0.8 + 0.4 =$	15.	$3.95 + 2.05 =$
4.	$0.8 + 0.45 =$	16.	$6.1 - 2.1 =$
5.	$1 - 0.5 =$	17.	$6 - 2.1 =$
6.	$1 - 0.3 =$	18.	$6.5 - 2.4 =$
7.	$2 - 1.99 =$	19.	$6.55 - 2.4 =$
8.	$2 - 0.99 =$	20.	$7 + 3.06 =$
9.	$2 + 1.98 =$	21.	$7.2 + 3.46 =$
10.	$2.03 + 3.1 =$	22.	$7.25 + 3.45 =$
11.	$2.03 + 3.01 =$	23.	$7 - 3.9 =$
12.	$3.3 + 2.09 =$	24.	$7.2 - 3.9 =$

Math Sprints 4

425 B | Add or subtract. | First Half

1.	0.6 + 0.3 + 0.1 =	13.	1.75 + 2.2 + 2 =
2.	0.7 + 0.2 + 0.1 =	14.	3.75 + 2.15 + 0.1 =
3.	0.8 + 0.2 + 0.1 =	15.	3.95 + 2.05 =
4.	0.8 + 0.32 =	16.	6.1 – 2.1 =
5.	2 – 1.6 =	17.	6 – 2.1 =
6.	2 – 1.3 =	18.	6.5 – 2.4 =
7.	2 – 1.98 =	19.	6.55 – 2.4 =
8.	3 – 1.98 =	20.	7 + 2.96 + 0.1 =
9.	2 + 1.9 + 0.08 =	21.	7.2 + 3.46 =
10.	2.03 + 1.5 + 0.2 =	22.	7.25 + 3.45 =
11.	2.03 + 1.07 =	23.	7 – 3.9 =
12.	3.3 + 2.04 + 0.05 =	24.	7.2 – 3.9 =

425 B	Add or subtract.	Second Half

1.	$0.4 + 0.3 + 0.3 =$	13.	$1.75 + 2.1 + 2 =$
2.	$0.4 + 0.3 + 0.3 =$	14.	$3.75 + 2.05 + 0.1 =$
3.	$0.8 + 0.2 + 0.2 =$	15.	$3.95 + 2.05 =$
4.	$0.8 + 0.45 =$	16.	$6.1 - 2.1 =$
5.	$2 - 1.5 =$	17.	$6 - 2.1 =$
6.	$2 - 1.3 =$	18.	$6.5 - 2.4 =$
7.	$2 - 1.99 =$	19.	$6.55 - 2.4 =$
8.	$3 - 1.99 =$	20.	$7 + 2.96 + 0.1 =$
9.	$2 + 1.9 + 0.08 =$	21.	$7.2 + 3.46 =$
10.	$2.03 + 1.5 + 1.6 =$	22.	$7.25 + 3.45 =$
11.	$2.03 + 3.01 =$	23.	$7 - 3.9 =$
12.	$3.3 + 2.04 + 0.05 =$	24.	$7.2 - 3.9 =$

426 A | Write as a whole or mixed number. | First Half

1.	0.1 =	16.	2.25 =
2.	0.3 =	17.	2.7 =
3.	0.5 =	18.	2.8 =
4.	0.6 =	19.	2.88 =
5.	0.9 =	20.	3.65 =
6.	1.9 =	21.	3.75 =
7.	0.2 =	22.	3.05 =
8.	0.03 =	23.	3.04 =
9.	0.05 =	24.	4.1 =
10.	0.09 =	25.	4.01 =
11.	1.25 =	26.	4.11 =
12.	1.5 =	27.	4.08 =
13.	1.75 =	28.	4.8 =
14.	2.2 =	29.	4.9 =
15.	2.04 =	30.	4.95 =

426 A Write as a whole or mixed number. Second Half

1.	0.3 =	16.	2.4 =
2.	0.1 =	17.	2.9 =
3.	0.7 =	18.	2.6 =
4.	0.4 =	19.	2.77 =
5.	0.9 =	20.	3.6 =
6.	1.7 =	21.	3.75 =
7.	0.2 =	22.	3.05 =
8.	0.07 =	23.	3.1 =
9.	0.05 =	24.	4.1 =
10.	0.09 =	25.	4.01 =
11.	1.5 =	26.	4.11 =
12.	1.4 =	27.	4.08 =
13.	1.75 =	28.	4.8 =
14.	2.2	29.	4.9 =
15.	2.04	30.	4.95 =

426 B Write the sum as a whole or mixed number. First Half

1.	0.05 + 0.05 =	16.	2.15 + 0.1 =
2.	0.2 + 0.1 =	17.	2.5 + 0.2 =
3.	0.3 + 0.2 =	18.	2.5 + 0.3 =
4.	0.1 + 0.5 =	19.	2.75 + 0.13 =
5.	0.2 + 0.7 =	20.	3.45 + 0.2 =
6.	1.4 + 0.5 =	21.	3.5 + 0.25 =
7.	0.1 + 0.1 =	22.	3.02 + 0.03 =
8.	0.01 + 0.02 =	23.	3.03 + 0.01 =
9.	0.01 + 0.04 =	24.	3.1 + 1 =
10.	0.03 + 0.06 =	25.	4 + 0.01 =
11.	1.15 + 0.1 =	26.	4.09 + 0.02 =
12.	0.75 + 0.75 =	27.	2.04 + 2.04 =
13.	1 + 0.75 =	28.	2.4 + 2.4 =
14.	2 + 0.2 =	29.	4 + 0.9 =
15.	2.02 + 0.02 =	30.	4.49 + 0.46 =

426 B Write the sum as a whole or mixed number. Second Half

1.	0.1 + 0.2 =	16.	2.15 + 0.25 =
2.	0.05 + 0.05 =	17.	2.5 + 0.4 =
3.	0.3 + 0.4 =	18.	2.5 + 0.1 =
4.	0.1 + 0.3 =	19.	2.75 + 0.02 =
5.	0.3 + 0.6 =	20.	3.45 + 0.15 =
6.	1.2 + 0.5 =	21.	3.5 + 0.25 =
7.	0.1 + 0.1 =	22.	3.02 + 0.03 =
8.	0.05 + 0.02 =	23.	3.03 + 0.07 =
9.	0.01 + 0.04 =	24.	2.1 + 2 =
10.	0.03 + 0.06 =	25.	4 + 0.01 =
11.	1.15 + 0.35 =	26.	4.09 + 0.02 =
12.	0.75 + 0.65 =	27.	1.04 + 3.04 =
13.	1 + 0.75 =	28.	2.4 + 2.4 =
14.	1 + 1.2 =	29.	3 + 1.9 =
15.	2.02 + 0.02 =	30.	4.39 + 0.56 =

427 A — Write in decimal form. — First Half

1.	$\frac{1}{10}$ =	16.	$2\frac{75}{100}$ =
2.	$\frac{3}{10}$ =	17.	$3\frac{4}{100}$ =
3.	$\frac{5}{10}$ =	18.	$3\frac{4}{10}$ =
4.	$\frac{9}{10}$ =	19.	$3\frac{28}{100}$ =
5.	$\frac{25}{100}$ =	20.	$4\frac{5}{10}$ =
6.	$\frac{50}{100}$ =	21.	$4\frac{5}{100}$ =
7.	$\frac{78}{100}$ =	22.	$4\frac{80}{100}$ =
8.	$\frac{1}{100}$ =	23.	$5\frac{2}{10}$ =
9.	$\frac{5}{100}$ =	24.	$5\frac{7}{10}$ =
10.	$1\frac{1}{10}$ =	25.	$5\frac{7}{100}$ =
11.	$2\frac{6}{10}$ =	26.	$5\frac{75}{100}$ =
12.	$1\frac{1}{100}$ =	27.	$6\frac{1}{10}$ =
13.	$1\frac{15}{100}$ =	28.	$6\frac{10}{100}$ =
14.	$2\frac{3}{100}$ =	29.	$6\frac{26}{100}$ =
15.	$2\frac{35}{100}$ =	30.	$7\frac{100}{100}$ =

427 A — Write in decimal form. — Second Half

1.	$\frac{2}{10}$ =	16.	$2\frac{95}{100}$ =
2.	$\frac{4}{10}$ =	17.	$3\frac{5}{100}$ =
3.	$\frac{6}{10}$ =	18.	$3\frac{7}{10}$ =
4.	$\frac{7}{10}$ =	19.	$3\frac{38}{100}$ =
5.	$\frac{35}{100}$ =	20.	$4\frac{5}{10}$ =
6.	$\frac{50}{100}$ =	21.	$4\frac{15}{100}$ =
7.	$\frac{88}{100}$ =	22.	$4\frac{85}{100}$ =
8.	$\frac{2}{100}$ =	23.	$5\frac{1}{10}$ =
9.	$\frac{5}{100}$ =	24.	$5\frac{4}{10}$ =
10.	$1\frac{3}{10}$ =	25.	$5\frac{7}{100}$ =
11.	$2\frac{4}{10}$ =	26.	$5\frac{75}{100}$ =
12.	$1\frac{21}{100}$ =	27.	$6\frac{1}{10}$ =
13.	$1\frac{15}{100}$ =	28.	$6\frac{10}{100}$ =
14.	$2\frac{3}{100}$ =	29.	$6\frac{26}{100}$ =
15.	$2\frac{38}{100}$ =	30.	$7\frac{100}{100}$ =

427 B Write in decimal form. First Half

1.	$\frac{1}{10}$ =	16.	$2\frac{75}{100}$ =
2.	$\frac{3}{10}$ =	17.	$3\frac{4}{100}$ =
3.	$\frac{5}{10}$ =	18.	$3\frac{8}{20}$ =
4.	$\frac{9}{10}$ =	19.	$3\frac{28}{100}$ =
5.	$\frac{25}{100}$ =	20.	$4\frac{15}{30}$ =
6.	$\frac{100}{200}$ =	21.	$4\frac{50}{1000}$ =
7.	$\frac{78}{100}$ =	22.	$4\frac{160}{200}$ =
8.	$\frac{10}{1000}$ =	23.	$5\frac{20}{100}$ =
9.	$\frac{25}{500}$ =	24.	$5\frac{14}{20}$ =
10.	$1\frac{1}{10}$ =	25.	$5\frac{14}{200}$ =
11.	$2\frac{6}{10}$ =	26.	$5\frac{150}{200}$ =
12.	$1\frac{1}{100}$ =	27.	$6\frac{100}{1000}$ =
13.	$1\frac{30}{200}$ =	28.	$6\frac{40}{400}$ =
14.	$2\frac{6}{200}$ =	29.	$6\frac{52}{200}$ =
15.	$2\frac{350}{1000}$ =	30.	$7\frac{100}{100}$ =

427 B Write in decimal form. Second Half

1.	$\frac{2}{10} =$	16.	$2\frac{95}{100} =$
2.	$\frac{4}{10} =$	17.	$3\frac{5}{100} =$
3.	$\frac{6}{10} =$	18.	$3\frac{7}{10} =$
4.	$\frac{7}{10} =$	19.	$3\frac{38}{100} =$
5.	$\frac{35}{100} =$	20.	$4\frac{20}{40} =$
6.	$\frac{150}{300} =$	21.	$4\frac{150}{1000} =$
7.	$\frac{88}{100} =$	22.	$4\frac{85}{100} =$
8.	$\frac{20}{1000} =$	23.	$5\frac{20}{200} =$
9.	$\frac{50}{1000} =$	24.	$5\frac{2}{5} =$
10.	$1\frac{3}{10} =$	25.	$5\frac{21}{300} =$
11.	$2\frac{2}{5} =$	26.	$5\frac{150}{200} =$
12.	$1\frac{21}{100} =$	27.	$6\frac{100}{1000} =$
13.	$1\frac{45}{300} =$	28.	$6\frac{50}{500} =$
14.	$2\frac{6}{200} =$	29.	$6\frac{26}{100} =$
15.	$2\frac{380}{1000} =$	30.	$7\frac{100}{100} =$

428 A | Divide. | First Half

1.	$8 \div 2 =$	13.	$0.6 \div 2 =$
2.	$0.8 \div 2 =$	14.	$0.64 \div 2 =$
3.	$0.08 \div 2 =$	15.	$6.4 \div 2 =$
4.	$0.08 \div 4 =$	16.	$0.64 \div 4 =$
5.	$15 \div 3 =$	17.	$0.64 \div 8 =$
6.	$1.5 \div 3 =$	18.	$32 \div 4 =$
7.	$0.15 \div 3 =$	19.	$0.32 \div 4 =$
8.	$0.15 \div 5 =$	20.	$0.32 \div 8 =$
9.	$36 \div 4 =$	21.	$0.32 \div 2 =$
10.	$3.6 \div 4 =$	22.	$3.12 \div 3 =$
11.	$0.36 \div 4 =$	23.	$4.26 \div 6 =$
12.	$0.36 \div 9 =$	24.	$8.48 \div 8 =$

428 A | Divide. | Second Half

1.	$6 \div 2 =$	13.	$0.8 \div 2 =$
2.	$0.6 \div 2 =$	14.	$0.84 \div 2 =$
3.	$0.06 \div 2 =$	15.	$8.4 \div 2 =$
4.	$0.06 \div 3 =$	16.	$0.84 \div 4 =$
5.	$18 \div 3 =$	17.	$0.64 \div 8 =$
6.	$1.8 \div 3 =$	18.	$32 \div 4 =$
7.	$0.18 \div 3 =$	19.	$0.32 \div 4 =$
8.	$0.18 \div 6 =$	20.	$0.32 \div 8 =$
9.	$32 \div 4 =$	21.	$0.32 \div 2 =$
10.	$3.2 \div 4 =$	22.	$6.12 \div 3 =$
11.	$0.32 \div 4 =$	23.	$4.86 \div 6 =$
12.	$0.32 \div 8 =$	24.	$7.49 \div 7 =$

428 B — Divide. — First Half

1.	96 ÷ 24 =	13.	0.6 ÷ 2 =
2.	9.6 ÷ 24 =	14.	0.64 ÷ 2 =
3.	0.96 ÷ 24 =	15.	6.4 ÷ 2 =
4.	0.96 ÷ 48 =	16.	0.64 ÷ 4 =
5.	150 ÷ 30 =	17.	0.64 ÷ 8 =
6.	1.5 ÷ 3 =	18.	288 ÷ 36 =
7.	0.15 ÷ 3 =	19.	2.88 ÷ 36 =
8.	0.15 ÷ 5 =	20.	0.32 ÷ 8 =
9.	243 ÷ 27 =	21.	0.32 ÷ 2 =
10.	24.3 ÷ 27 =	22.	3.12 ÷ 3 =
11.	2.43 ÷ 27 =	23.	4.26 ÷ 6 =
12.	0.36 ÷ 9 =	24.	8.48 ÷ 8 =

428 B — Divide. — Second Half

1.	$72 \div 24 =$	13.	$1.6 \div 4 =$
2.	$7.2 \div 24 =$	14.	$2.94 \div 7 =$
3.	$0.72 \div 24 =$	15.	$8.4 \div 2 =$
4.	$0.12 \div 6 =$	16.	$0.84 \div 4 =$
5.	$180 \div 30 =$	17.	$0.64 \div 8 =$
6.	$1.8 \div 3 =$	18.	$288 \div 36 =$
7.	$0.18 \div 3 =$	19.	$2.88 \div 36 =$
8.	$0.18 \div 6 =$	20.	$0.32 \div 8 =$
9.	$216 \div 27 =$	21.	$0.32 \div 2 =$
10.	$21.6 \div 27 =$	22.	$12.24 \div 6 =$
11.	$2.16 \div 27 =$	23.	$4.86 \div 6 =$
12.	$0.32 \div 8 =$	24.	$8.\ 56 \div 8 =$

429 A | Multiply. | First Half

1.	6 x 3 =	11.	0.08 x 6 =
2.	0.6 x 3 =	12.	0.08 x 7 =
3.	0.06 x 3 =	13.	0.08 x 10 =
4.	3 x 6 =	14.	1.2 x 3 =
5.	0.3 x 6 =	15.	12 x 3 =
6.	0.03 x 6 =	16.	0.12 x 3 =
7.	7 x 4 =	17.	11 x 6 =
8.	0.7 x 4 =	18.	1.1 x 6 =
9.	0.07 x 4 =	19.	11.3 x 6 =
10.	0.08 x 3 =	20.	11.7 x 6 =

429 A | Multiply. | Second Half

1.	7 x 3 =	11.	0.08 x 5 =
2.	0.7 x 3 =	12.	0.08 x 6 =
3.	0.07 x 3 =	13.	0.09 x 10 =
4.	3 x 7 =	14.	1.1 x 3 =
5.	0.3 x 7 =	15.	11 x 3 =
6.	0.03 x 7 =	16.	0.11 x 3 =
7.	6 x 4 =	17.	12 x 6 =
8.	0.6 x 4 =	18.	1.2 x 6 =
9.	0.06 x 4 =	19.	11.3 x 6 =
10.	0.08 x 4 =	20.	11.7 x 6 =

429 B — Multiply or divide. — First Half

1.	3 x 2 x 3 =	11.	2 x 0.08 x 3 =
2.	0.2 x 3 x 3 =	12.	0.08 x 7 =
3.	0.02 x 3 x 3 =	13.	2 x 0.08 x 5 =
4.	54 ÷ 3 =	14.	0.4 x 3 x 3 =
5.	2 x 3 x 0.3 =	15.	324 ÷ 9 =
6.	2 x 0.03 x 3 =	16.	3 x 0.04 x 3 =
7.	112 ÷ 4 =	17.	462 ÷ 7 =
8.	2 x 0.7 x 2 =	18.	2 x 1.1 x 3 =
9.	2 x 0.07 x 2 =	19.	3 x 1.13 x 10 x 2 =
10.	3 x 0.02 x 4 =	20.	2 x 1.17 x 10 x 3 =

429 B — Multiply or divide. — Second Half

1.	7 x 3 =	11.	0.08 x 5 =
2.	0.7 x 3 =	12.	2 x 0.08 x 3 =
3.	0.07 x 3 =	13.	2 x 0.09 x 5 =
4.	63 ÷ 3 =	14.	1.1 x 3 =
5.	6.3 ÷ 3 =	15.	3 x 11 =
6.	0.63 ÷ 3 =	16.	0.11 x 3 =
7.	96 ÷ 4 =	17.	504 ÷ 7 =
8.	9.6 ÷ 4 =	18.	2 x 1.2 x 3 =
9.	0.96 ÷ 4 =	19.	3 x 1.13 x 10 x 2 =
10.	2 x 0.04 x 4 =	20.	2 x 1.17 x 10 x 3 =

Answers

401 A & B			First Half
1.	<	16.	=
2.	<	17.	<
3.	<	18.	=
4.	=	19.	>
5.	>	20.	>
6.	=	21.	<
7.	<	22.	=
8.	>	23.	<
9.	>	24.	<
10.	>	25.	<
11.	<	26.	>
12.	<	27.	=
13.	<	28.	>
14.	>	29.	>
15.	<	30.	<

402 A & B			First Half
1.	30	19.	830
2.	30	20.	940
3.	50	21.	940
4.	70	22.	1,000
5.	130	23.	1,010
6.	280	24.	1,290
7.	340	25.	1,300
8.	100	26.	1,320
9.	200	27.	1,410
10.	200	28.	1,500
11.	310	29.	1,560
12.	380	30.	1,680
13.	600	31.	1,880
14.	700	32.	2,000
15.	3,650	33.	2,020
16.	800	34.	2,090
17.	790	35.	2,500
18.	820	36.	10,000

403 A & B			First Half
1.	100	19.	5,800
2.	100	20.	5,900
3.	100	21.	6,000
4.	200	22.	7,000
5.	300	23.	10,000
6.	300	24.	10,300
7.	400	25.	10,300
8.	600	26.	10,500
9.	900	27.	10,400
10.	1,200	28.	10,500
11.	1,300	29.	12,600
12.	1,400	30.	12,700
13.	1,600	31.	12,900
14.	2,700	32.	20,000
15.	3,700	33.	20,000
16.	4,800	34.	21,100
17.	4,600	35.	21,600
18.	4,900	36.	30,000

401 A & B			Second Half
1.	<	16.	=
2.	<	17.	<
3.	<	18.	=
4.	=	19.	>
5.	>	20.	>
6.	=	21.	<
7.	<	22.	=
8.	>	23.	<
9.	>	24.	<
10.	>	25.	<
11.	<	26.	>
12.	<	27.	=
13.	<	28.	>
14.	>	29.	>
15.	<	30.	<

402 A & B			Second Half
1.	30	19.	830
2.	30	20.	940
3.	50	21.	940
4.	70	22.	1,000
5.	130	23.	1,010
6.	280	24.	1,290
7.	340	25.	1,300
8.	100	26.	1,320
9.	200	27.	1,410
10.	200	28.	1,500
11.	310	29.	1,560
12.	380	30.	1,680
13.	600	31.	1,880
14.	700	32.	2,000
15.	3,650	33.	2,020
16.	800	34.	2,090
17.	790	35.	2,500
18.	820	36.	10,000

403 A & B			Second Half
1.	100	19.	5,800
2.	100	20.	5,900
3.	100	21.	6,000
4.	200	22.	7,000
5.	300	23.	10,000
6.	300	24.	10,300
7.	400	25.	10,300
8.	600	26.	10,500
9.	900	27.	10,400
10.	1,200	28.	10,500
11.	1,300	29.	12,600
12.	1,400	30.	12,700
13.	1,600	31.	12,900
14.	2,700	32.	20,000
15.	3,700	33.	20,000
16.	4,800	34.	21,100
17.	4,600	35.	21,600
18.	4,900	36.	30,000

Answers

404 A & B			First Half
1.	0	19.	11,000
2.	0	20.	11,000
3.	0	21.	10,000
4.	1,000	22.	12,000
5.	2,000	23.	11,000
6.	2,000	24.	13,000
7.	2,000	25.	13,000
8.	3,000	26.	14,000
9.	3,000	27.	13,000
10.	3,000	28.	14,000
11.	4,000	29.	14,000
12.	4,000	30.	15,000
13.	5,000	31.	15,000
14.	6,000	32.	20,000
15.	7,000	33.	20,000
16.	8,000	34.	22,000
17.	9,000	35.	22,000
18.	9,000	36.	40,000

405 A & B			First Half
1.	T	16.	F
2.	T	17.	T
3.	T	18.	T
4.	T	19.	F
5.	T	20.	F
6.	T	21.	T
7.	F	22.	T
8.	F	23.	F
9.	T	24.	F
10.	T	25.	T
11.	F	26.	T
12.	F	27.	T
13.	T	28.	F
14.	F	29.	T
15.	T	30.	T

406 A & B			First Half
1.	T	13.	T
2.	T	14.	F
3.	T	15.	F
4.	T	16.	F
5.	F	17.	T
6.	F	18.	T
7.	T	19.	T
8.	F	20.	T
9.	T	21.	F
10.	T	22.	T
11.	F	23.	T
12.	F	24.	T

404 A & B			Second Half
1.	0	19.	11,000
2.	0	20.	11,000
3.	0	21.	10,000
4.	1,000	22.	12,000
5.	2,000	23.	11,000
6.	2,000	24.	13,000
7.	2,000	25.	13,000
8.	3,000	26.	14,000
9.	3,000	27.	13,000
10.	3,000	28.	14,000
11.	4,000	29.	14,000
12.	4,000	30.	15,000
13.	5,000	31.	15,000
14.	6,000	32.	20,000
15.	7,000	33.	20,000
16.	8,000	34.	22,000
17.	9,000	35.	22,000
18.	9,000	36.	40,000

405 A & B			Second Half
1.	T	16.	F
2.	T	17.	T
3.	T	18.	T
4.	T	19.	F
5.	T	20.	F
6.	T	21.	T
7.	F	22.	T
8.	F	23.	F
9.	T	24.	F
10.	T	25.	T
11.	F	26.	T
12.	F	27.	T
13.	T	28.	F
14.	F	29.	T
15.	T	30.	T

406 A & B			Second Half
1.	T	16.	T
2.	T	17.	F
3.	T	18.	F
4.	T	19.	F
5.	F	20.	T
6.	F	21.	T
7.	T	22.	T
8.	F	23.	T
9.	T	24.	F
10.	T	25.	T
11.	F	26.	T
12.	F	27.	T

Answers

407 A & B			First Half
1.	20	16.	111
2.	19	17.	110
3.	19	18.	129
4.	21	19.	130
5.	20	20.	130
6.	30	21.	131
7.	40	22.	146
8.	50	23.	145
9.	49	24.	147
10.	61	25.	149
11.	62	26.	159
12.	69	27.	160
13.	68	28.	169
14.	70	29.	168
15.	78	30.	238

408 A & B			First Half
1.	0	16.	110
2.	10	17.	100
3.	20	18.	110
4.	40	19.	111
5.	41	20.	120
6.	51	21.	119
7.	81	22.	130
8.	91	23.	120
9.	91	24.	121
10.	92	25.	131
11.	90	26.	141
12.	94	27.	151
13.	109	28.	150
14.	110	29.	149
15.	108	30.	61

409 A & B			First Half
1.	100	16.	400
2.	50	17.	245
3.	120	18.	245
4.	60	19.	200
5.	130	20.	175
6.	140	21.	165
7.	135	22.	185
8.	70	23.	175
9.	65	24.	155
10.	190	25.	150
11.	180	26.	145
12.	175	27.	160
13.	165	28.	155
14.	155	29.	200
15.	300	30.	310

407 A & B			Second Half
1.	40	16.	110
2.	39	17.	109
3.	29	18.	119
4.	22	19.	120
5.	21	20.	120
6.	40	21.	121
7.	50	22.	156
8.	60	23.	155
9.	59	24.	157
10.	72	25.	159
11.	73	26.	169
12.	79	27.	170
13.	78	28.	189
14.	80	29.	188
15.	88	30.	258

408 A & B			Second Half
1.	0	16.	100
2.	20	17.	90
3.	30	18.	80
4.	50	19.	91
5.	51	20.	100
6.	61	21.	99
7.	71	22.	110
8.	91	23.	100
9.	91	24.	101
10.	92	25.	111
11.	90	26.	121
12.	93	27.	131
13.	102	28.	140
14.	103	29.	139
15.	101	30.	51

409 A & B			Second Half
1.	80	16.	410
2.	40	17.	145
3.	60	18.	145
4.	30	19.	200
5.	90	20.	195
6.	110	21.	185
7.	115	22.	195
8.	60	23.	185
9.	55	24.	175
10.	280	25.	180
11.	270	26.	165
12.	275	27.	170
13.	265	28.	165
14.	255	29.	200
15.	400	30.	310

Answers

410 A & B	First Half		
1.	6	16.	20
2.	12	17.	30
3.	24	18.	30
4.	9	19.	35
5.	18	20.	45
6.	27	21.	60
7.	36	22.	65
8.	16	23.	55
9.	32	24.	44
10.	48	25.	36
11.	52	26.	32
12.	56	27.	24
13.	40	28.	28
14.	80	29.	48
15.	10	30.	52

411 A & B	First Half		
1.	2	16.	2
2.	3	17.	4
3.	6	18.	8
4.	12	19.	12
5.	3	20.	7
6.	5	21.	9
7.	7	22.	10
8.	8	23.	10
9.	9	24.	10
10.	11	25.	11
11.	3	26.	12
12.	5	27.	13
13.	8	28.	10
14.	9	29.	12
15.	11	30.	13

412 A & B	First Half		
1.	6	16.	28
2.	12	17.	42
3.	18	18.	49
4.	24	19.	63
5.	36	20.	56
6.	42	21.	70
7.	54	22.	8
8.	48	23.	9
9.	2	24.	6
10.	4	25.	16
11.	8	26.	32
12.	6	27.	48
13.	7	28.	56
14.	9	29.	72
15.	14	30.	64

410 A & B	Second Half		
1.	4	16.	15
2.	8	17.	20
3.	16	18.	30
4.	6	19.	35
5.	12	20.	45
6.	24	21.	55
7.	30	22.	60
8.	12	23.	65
9.	24	24.	40
10.	36	25.	32
11.	48	26.	28
12.	52	27.	24
13.	40	28.	16
14.	80	29.	48
15.	10	30.	52

411 A & B	Second Half		
1.	3	16.	1
2.	4	17.	2
3.	7	18.	4
4.	10	19.	3
5.	2	20.	6
6.	3	21.	8
7.	4	22.	10
8.	6	23.	10
9.	7	24.	10
10.	9	25.	11
11.	2	26.	12
12.	4	27.	13
13.	6	28.	14
14.	7	29.	15
15.	8	30.	17

412 A & B	Second Half		
1.	12	16.	35
2.	18	17.	28
3.	30	18.	42
4.	24	19.	56
5.	36	20.	49
6.	48	21.	63
7.	54	22.	9
8.	66	23.	10
9.	2	24.	7
10.	3	25.	16
11.	6	26.	40
12.	7	27.	24
13.	5	28.	56
14.	9	29.	72
15.	21	30.	64

Answers

413 A & B			First Half
1.	16	16.	2
2.	18	17.	3
3.	24	18.	4
4.	27	19.	5
5.	32	20.	6
6.	36	21.	8
7.	48	22.	7
8.	54	23.	9
9.	56	24.	4
10.	56	25.	5
11.	63	26.	6
12.	40	27.	8
13.	48	28.	10
14.	64	29.	9
15.	80	30.	11

414 A & B			First Half
1.	9	16.	3
2.	18	17.	6
3.	24	18.	8
4.	12	19.	3
5.	24	20.	6
6.	32	21.	9
7.	36	22.	3
8.	18	23.	4
9.	30	24.	6
10.	36	25.	8
11.	48	26.	6
12.	42	27.	8
13.	49	28.	7
14.	56	29.	5
15.	63	30.	12

415 A & B			First Half
1.	60	16.	600
2.	100	17.	1,200
3.	160	18.	180
4.	80	19.	1,800
5.	100	20.	200
6.	180	21.	400
7.	190	22.	600
8.	200	23.	800
9.	400	24.	1,200
10.	140	25.	420
11.	280	26.	210
12.	420	27.	630
13.	560	28.	540
14.	280	29.	270
15.	2,800	30.	810

413 A & B			Second Half
1.	8	16.	2
2.	16	17.	3
3.	18	18.	4
4.	27	19.	5
5.	40	20.	6
6.	45	21.	9
7.	32	22.	8
8.	36	23.	7
9.	48	24.	3
10.	48	25.	6
11.	63	26.	8
12.	40	27.	7
13.	48	28.	10
14.	64	29.	9
15.	80	30.	11

414 A & B			Second Half
1.	6	16.	4
2.	12	17.	7
3.	18	18.	5
4.	32	19.	3
5.	8	20.	6
6.	16	21.	9
7.	24	22.	3
8.	12	23.	4
9.	18	24.	6
10.	24	25.	8
11.	36	26.	6
12.	42	27.	8
13.	49	28.	7
14.	77	29.	5
15.	70	30.	12

415 A & B			Second Half
1.	70	16.	700
2.	100	17.	1,400
3.	170	18.	210
4.	90	19.	2,100
5.	100	20.	400
6.	190	21.	800
7.	180	22.	1,200
8.	300	23.	800
9.	600	24.	1,200
10.	160	25.	420
11.	320	26.	210
12.	480	27.	630
13.	640	28.	540
14.	280	29.	270
15.	2,800	30.	810

Answers

416A & B			First Half
1.	80	11.	60
2.	8	12.	3
3.	80	13.	63
4.	800	14.	630
5.	8	15.	63
6.	80	16.	70
7.	840	17.	2
8.	84	18.	72
9.	840	19.	36
10.	84	20.	10

417 A & B			First Half
1.	2	13.	18
2.	2	14.	28
3.	2	15.	35
4.	3	16.	8
5.	3	17.	40
6.	9	18.	45
7.	12	19.	64
8.	30	20.	45
9.	12	21.	8
10.	25	22.	40
11.	15	23.	56
12.	21	24.	117

418 A & B			First Half
1.	$\frac{2}{3}$	11.	$\frac{1}{2}$
2.	$\frac{2}{5}$	12.	$\frac{5}{8}$
3.	$\frac{1}{3}$	13.	$\frac{7}{8}$
4.	$\frac{3}{4}$	14.	1
5.	$\frac{1}{2}$	15.	$\frac{4}{7}$
6.	1	16.	$\frac{1}{2}$
7.	$\frac{1}{2}$	17.	$\frac{3}{16}$
8.	$\frac{1}{5}$	18.	$\frac{7}{9}$
9.	$\frac{3}{10}$	19.	$\frac{5}{6}$
10.	$\frac{4}{5}$	20.	1

416 A & B			Second Half
1.	70	11.	50
2.	7	12.	5
3.	70	13.	56
4.	700	14.	560
5.	7	15.	56
6.	70	16.	70
7.	720	17.	2
8.	72	18.	72
9.	720	19.	36
10.	72	20.	10

417 A & B			Second Half
1.	2	16.	35
2.	2	17.	28
3.	3	18.	18
4.	3	19.	8
5.	2	20.	40
6.	9	21.	45
7.	12	22.	64
8.	21	23.	45
9.	12	24.	8
10.	25	25.	40
11.	15	26.	56
12.	30	27.	135

418 A & B			Second Half
1.	$\frac{2}{5}$	11.	$\frac{5}{8}$
2.	$\frac{2}{3}$	12.	$\frac{1}{2}$
3.	$\frac{1}{3}$	13.	$\frac{7}{8}$
4.	$\frac{3}{4}$	14.	1
5.	1	15.	$\frac{4}{7}$
6.	$\frac{1}{2}$	16.	$\frac{1}{2}$
7.	$\frac{1}{2}$	17.	$\frac{3}{16}$
8.	$\frac{1}{5}$	18.	$\frac{7}{9}$
9.	$\frac{3}{10}$	19.	$\frac{5}{6}$
10.	$\frac{4}{5}$	20.	1

Answers

419 A & B			First Half
1.	2/3	16.	5/8
2.	2/5	17.	1/2
3.	4/5	18.	2/3
4.	4/7	19.	1/2
5.	6/7	20.	3/8
6.	1/4	21.	7/10
7.	3/8	22.	1
8.	5/8	23.	4/5
9.	1/3	24.	3/5
10.	5/9	25.	1/10
11.	2/3	26.	2/5
12.	1/3	27.	1/6
13.	3/4	28.	5/8
14.	1/3	29.	1/4
15.	2/3	30.	0

420 A & B			First Half
1.	1 1/3	16.	1 1/7
2.	1 1/5	17.	2
3.	1 1/9	18.	1 6/7
4.	1 1/7	19.	1 3/7
5.	1 3/5	20.	1 5/7
6.	1 4/5	21.	3 1/5
7.	1 1/4	22.	3 4/5
8.	2 2/3	23.	2
9.	3 2/3	24.	1 1/3
10.	1 1/6	25.	1 4/9
11.	1 4/5	26.	1 7/9
12.	1 3/5	27.	2 2/9
13.	2 1/5	28.	2 3/10
14.	2 2/5	29.	2 9/10
15.	2 4/5	30.	3 1/10

421 A & B			First Half
1.	2	11.	$2\frac{1}{2}$
2.	2	12.	$4\frac{1}{2}$
3.	$1\frac{3}{4}$	13.	$4\frac{3}{4}$
4.	$2\frac{2}{5}$	14.	$7\frac{1}{2}$
5.	2	15.	$2\frac{3}{5}$
6.	2	16.	$3\frac{1}{9}$
7.	4	17.	$4\frac{1}{6}$
8.	$3\frac{3}{5}$	18.	$6\frac{1}{5}$
9.	$2\frac{1}{8}$	19.	4
10.	$2\frac{1}{2}$	20.	8

419 A & B			Second Half
1.	2/5	16.	3/4
2.	2/3	17.	2/3
3.	4/7	18.	1/2
4.	4/5	19.	1/2
5.	6/7	20.	3/8
6.	1/3	21.	7/10
7.	3/8	22.	1
8.	5/8	23.	4/5
9.	1/3	24.	3/5
10.	5/9	25.	1/10
11.	2/3	26.	2/5
12.	1/3	27.	1/6
13.	3/4	28.	5/8
14.	1/3	29.	1/4
15.	2/3	30.	0

420 A & B			Second Half
1.	1 1/2	16.	1 1/12
2.	1 1/6	17.	2
3.	1 1/8	18.	1 6/7
4.	1 1/7	19.	1 3/7
5.	1 2/5	20.	1 5/7
6.	1 4/5	21.	3 1/5
7.	1 1/4	22.	3 4/5
8.	2 2/3	23.	2
9.	3 1/3	24.	1 1/3
10.	1 5/6	25.	1 4/9
11.	1 4/5	26.	1 7/9
12.	1 3/5	27.	2 2/9
13.	2 1/5	28.	2 3/10
14.	2 2/5	29.	2 9/10
15.	2 4/5	30.	3 1/10

421 A & B			Second Half
1.	2	11.	$2\frac{1}{2}$
2.	2	12.	$4\frac{1}{2}$
3.	$1\frac{2}{3}$	13.	$4\frac{3}{4}$
4.	$2\frac{3}{5}$	14.	$7\frac{1}{2}$
5.	3	15.	$2\frac{3}{5}$
6.	2	16.	$3\frac{1}{9}$
7.	4	17.	$4\frac{1}{6}$
8.	$3\frac{3}{5}$	18.	$6\frac{1}{5}$
9.	$2\frac{1}{8}$	19.	4
10.	$2\frac{1}{2}$	20.	8

Answers

422 A & B	First Half		
1.	3/2	16.	11/3
2.	5/4	17.	27/8
3.	7/6	18.	31/8
4.	7/4	19.	17/4
5.	11/6	20.	14/3
6.	15/8	21.	23/5
7.	9/4	22.	22/5
8.	7/3	23.	25/6
9.	8/3	24.	30/7
10.	11/4	25.	33/8
11.	12/5	26.	43/10
12.	18/7	27.	46/9
13.	17/6	28.	49/9
14.	7/2	29.	50/9
15.	16/5	30.	52/9

423 A & B	First Half		
1.	5	13.	10
2.	9	14.	20
3.	2	15.	40
4.	4	16.	80
5.	2	17.	25
6.	6	18.	75
7.	6	19.	10
8.	12	20.	20
9.	3	21.	9
10.	9	22.	27
11.	15	23.	2/3
12.	21	24.	3/5

424 A & B	First Half		
1.	4	16.	4
2.	0.4	17.	4.2
3.	0.04	18.	8.6
4.	2.2	19.	9.1
5.	0.22	20.	10.5
6.	2.02	21.	1.33
7.	0.9	22.	0.57
8.	1.3	23.	0.6
9.	1.3	24.	2.6
10.	0.13	25.	23.59
11.	1.2	26.	25.18
12.	2.5	27.	31.27
13.	2.9	28.	32.73
14.	3	29.	32.07
15.	3.9	30.	40.98

422 A & B	Second Half		
1.	4/3	16.	17/5
2.	3/2	17.	26/7
3.	6/5	18.	31/8
4.	5/3	19.	17/4
5.	11/7	20.	14/3
6.	15/8	21.	19/4
7.	9/4	22.	22/5
8.	7/3	23.	25/6
9.	8/3	24.	30/7
10.	11/4	25.	33/8
11.	12/5	26.	43/10
12.	18/7	27.	46/9
13.	17/6	28.	49/9
14.	7/2	29.	50/9
15.	16/5	30.	52/9

423 A & B	Second Half		
1.	3	16.	5
2.	6	17.	10
3.	3	18.	20
4.	6	19.	40
5.	3	20.	25
6.	9	21.	75
7.	3	22.	10
8.	6	23.	20
9.	3	24.	9
10.	9	25.	27
11.	15	26.	3/8
12.	21	27.	4/5

424 A & B	Second Half		
1.	2	16.	4
2.	0.2	17.	4.2
3.	0.02	18.	8.6
4.	1.1	19.	9.1
5.	0.11	20.	10.5
6.	1.01	21.	1.33
7.	0.5	22.	0.57
8.	1.1	23.	0.6
9.	1.2	24.	2.6
10.	0.09	25.	23.59
11.	1.2	26.	25.18
12.	1.5	27.	31.27
13.	1.8	28.	22.43
14.	2	29.	22.08
15.	2.9	30.	30.98

Answers

425 A & B			First Half
1.	1	13.	5.95
2.	1	14.	6
3.	1.1	15.	6
4.	1.12	16.	4
5.	0.4	17.	3.9
6.	0.7	18.	4.1
7.	0.02	19.	4.15
8.	1.02	20.	10.06
9.	3.98	21.	10.66
10.	3.73	22.	10.7
11.	3.1	23.	3.1
12.	5.39	24.	3.3

426 A & B			First Half
1.	1/10	16.	2 1/4
2.	3/10	17.	2 7/10
3.	1/2	18.	2 4/5
4.	3/5	19.	2 22/25
5.	9/10	20.	3 13/20
6.	1 9/10	21.	3 3/4
7.	1/5	22.	3 1/20
8.	3/100	23.	3 1/25
9.	1/20	24.	4 1/10
10.	9/100	25.	4 1/100
11.	1 1/4	26.	4 11/100
12.	1 1/2	27.	4 2/25
13.	1 3/4	28.	4 4/5
14.	2 1/5	29.	4 9/10
15.	2 1/25	30.	4 19/20

427 A & B			First Half
1.	0.1	16.	2.75
2.	0.3	17.	3.04
3.	0.5	18.	3.4
4.	0.9	19.	3.28
5.	0.25	20.	4.5
6.	0.5	21.	4.05
7.	0.78	22.	4.8
8.	0.01	23.	5.2
9.	0.05	24.	5.7
10.	1.1	25.	5.07
11.	2.6	26.	5.75
12.	1.01	27.	6.1
13.	1.15	28.	6.1
14.	2.03	29.	6.26
15.	2.35	30.	8

425 A & B			Second Half
1.	1	16.	5.85
2.	1	17.	5.9
3.	1.2	18.	6
4.	1.25	19.	4
5.	0.5	20.	3.9
6.	0.7	21.	4.1
7.	0.01	22.	4.15
8.	1.01	23.	10.06
9.	3.98	24.	10.66
10.	5.13	25.	10.7
11.	5.04	26.	3.1
12.	5.39	27.	3.3

426 A & B			Second Half
1.	3/10	16.	2 2/5
2.	1/10	17.	2 9/10
3.	7/10	18.	2 3/5
4.	2/5	19.	2 77/100
5.	9/10	20.	3 3/5
6.	1 7/10	21.	3 3/4
7.	1/5	22.	3 1/20
8.	7/100	23.	3 1/10
9.	1/20	24.	4 1/10
10.	9/100	25.	4 1/100
11.	1 1/2	26.	4 11/100
12.	1 2/5	27.	4 2/25
13.	1 3/4	28.	4 4/5
14.	2 1/5	29.	4 9/10
15.	2 1/25	30.	4 19/20

427 A & B			Second Half
1.	0.2	16.	2.95
2.	0.4	17.	3.05
3.	0.6	18.	3.7
4.	0.7	19.	3.38
5.	0.35	20.	4.5
6.	0.5	21.	4.15
7.	0.88	22.	4.85
8.	0.02	23.	5.1
9.	0.05	24.	5.4
10.	1.3	25.	5.07
11.	2.4	26.	5.75
12.	1.21	27.	6.1
13.	1.15	28.	6.1
14.	2.03	29.	6.26
15.	2.38	30.	8

Answers

428 A & B			First Half
1.	4	13.	0.3
2.	0.4	14.	0.32
3.	0.04	15.	3.2
4.	0.02	16.	0.16
5.	5	17.	0.08
6.	0.5	18.	8
7.	0.05	19.	0.08
8.	0.03	20.	0.04
9.	9	21.	0.16
10.	0.9	22.	1.04
11.	0.09	23.	0.71
12.	0.04	24.	1.06

400A & B			First Half
1.	18	11.	0.48
2.	1.8	12.	0.56
3.	0.18	13.	0.8
4.	18	14.	3.6
5.	1.8	15.	36
6.	0.18	16.	0.36
7.	28	17.	66
8.	2.8	18.	6.6
9.	0.28	19.	67.8
10.	0.24	20.	70.2

428 A & B			Second Half
1.	3	16.	0.4
2.	0.3	17.	0.42
3.	0.03	18.	4.2
4.	0.02	19.	0.21
5.	6	20.	0.08
6.	0.6	21.	8
7.	0.06	22.	0.08
8.	0.03	23.	0.04
9.	8	24.	0.16
10.	0.8	25.	2.04
11.	0.08	26.	0.81
12.	0.04	27.	1.07

400 A & B			Second Half
1.	21	11.	0.4
2.	2.1	12.	0.48
3.	0.21	13.	0.9
4.	21	14.	3.3
5.	2.1	15.	33
6.	0.21	16.	0.33
7.	24	17.	72
8.	2.4	18.	7.2
9.	0.24	19.	67.8
10.	0.32	20.	70.2